PREFACE

THIS book contains a general description of the common grasses and legumes with which the British farmer is concerned. It is intended as a guide to the identification of the various species in the field, and has been written to meet the needs of farmers, schools, young farmers' classes and Agricultural colleges.

The authors are indebted to Dr. R. A. Roberts, Mr. G. W. Olive, M.A., and to various members of the Welsh Plant Breeding Station for taking a practical interest in the preparation of the book ; to the late Professor S. P. Mercer for supplying the keys to the vegetative organs of both grasses and legumes ; and to the late Mr. T. A. Dymes, Mr. H. J. Goddard (Dunns Farm Seeds, Ltd.) and Mr. Frank Hughes for supplying material.

They are also indebted to Mr. T. H. Davies, B.Sc. and Mr. A. Voysey, B.Sc. for improvements in the second edition, and to Mr. B. W. H. Coulson, M.A., for valuable assistance with the proofs.

The authors are very much indebted to Dr. D. H. Robinson for his assistance in the preparation of the third edition.

J. O. T.
L. J. D.

v

Common British
grasses and Legumes

COMMON BRITISH
GRASSES AND LEGUMES

COMMON BRITISH
GRASSES AND LEGUMES

BY

J. O. THOMAS, M.Sc., N.D.A., N.D.D.

(Principal, Lackham School of Agriculture, Wilts.)

AND

L. J. DAVIES

WITH 50 ILLUSTRATIONS

LONGMANS, GREEN AND CO.
LONDON ♦ NEW YORK ♦ TORONTO

LONGMANS, GREEN AND CO LTD
6 & 7 CLIFFORD STREET LONDON W 1

ALSO AT MELBOURNE AND CAPE TOWN

LONGMANS, GREEN AND CO INC
55 FIFTH AVENUE, NEW YORK 3

LONGMANS, GREEN AND CO
215 VICTORIA STREET, TORONTO 1

ORIENT LONGMANS LTD
BOMBAY CALCUTTA MADRAS

First Published in 1938
Second Edition by Photo-Litho process 1946
Third Edition 1949
New Impression 1952
New Impression 1954

Printed in Great Britain

CONTENTS ·

CHAPTER	PAGE
1. The Morphology of Some Common British Grasses .	1
2. Characters which Influence the Agricultural Value of Grasses	9
3. Key to the Vegetative Characters of Some Common Grasses	12
4. Botanical Descriptions of Grasses . . .	18
5. Leguminosae (Clover Family)	74
6. Key to the Vegetative Characters of Some Common Legumes	80
7. Botanical Descriptions of Clovers and Other Members of Leguminosae	82
References	114
Glossary	115
Index	118

CHAPTER 1

THE MORPHOLOGY OF SOME COMMON BRITISH GRASSES

(For the meaning of unfamiliar technical terms, the reader is advised to refer to the Glossary on page 115).

THE morphological features of grasses and cereals may be studied under two separate headings : (*a*) the floral organs, and (*b*) the vegetative organs.

The Floral Organs.

The flowers of grasses, although not conspicuous, possess all those parts which are essential for the production of seed. They are usually grouped together to form numerous spikelets, which are arranged in a racemose order, on a main stem or culm to form the inflorescence (Fig. 1 A).

The Inflorescence.—The form of the inflorescence varies greatly in different species, and is determined by the way in which the spikelets are attached to the main axis. In some species the spikelets are borne directly upon the main stem, forming an inflorescence termed a spike (Fig. 1 A), whereas in others they are borne on short simple branches to form a raceme or spike-like panicle (Fig. 6 A). In very many cases also the spikelets are supported on secondary, tertiary and further divided branches to form a panicle (Fig. 5 A). Such panicles appear to be close, spreading or drooping, according to the relative length of the branches.

The Spikelet.—A spikelet normally consists of an axis, at the base of which are borne a pair of opposite bracts, commonly called the outer and inner empty glumes. These glumes, although usually two in number, may vary from one in Italian Rye-grass (Fig. 1 B) to four in Sweet Vernal (Fig. 8).

Immediately above the empty glumes, and arranged in a similar manner, are two further bracts, termed the outer and inner pales, and in between which lies the actual flower (Fig. 1 C). The pales often differ from the empty glumes in possessing bristle-like structures called awns (Fig. 1 E). These may be terminal, dorsal or basal, according to whether they arise from the tip, middle or base of the pale.

The number of flowers in each spikelet varies from one to several in different species, e.g. Timothy and Tall Oat Grass always possess one and two flowers respectively, while in Italian Rye-grass there may be several flowers per spikelet (Fig. 1 c).

The Flower.—A typical flower (Fig. 1 D), which is protected on each side by the outer and inner pales, is composed of three hypogynous stamens (except in Sweet Vernal which possesses two) and one carpel. At the base of the ovary are two small scale-like structures termed lodicules, which may be clearly seen during the time of fertilisation. The filaments of the stamens are long and slender, and are attached to long anthers. The carpel consists of a small ovoid ovary, which frequently bears a pair of divergent feathery stigmas at its apex.

Grasses are wind-pollinated and cross-fertilised, though self-fertilisation often occurs. At the time of flowering the lodicules swell and spread apart the pales, thus exposing the feathery stigmas. About the same time the filaments of the stamens grow rapidly, and push out the anthers. The anthers then burst, and the pollen grains are distributed by the wind and caught by the feathery stigmas of other grasses to pollinate only those of the same species. In a short time afterwards the pales close up on the fertilised ovary, which then develops into a fruit. In some cases, such as Wheat, the flowers are cleistogamous, and fertilisation is often accomplished before the opening of the pales.

The Fruit or Commercial Seed.—During its formation the seed-coat fuses with the ovary wall to form a one-seeded fruit (commonly called a seed), termed a " caryopsis "; a typical example of this is seen in the wheat grain (Fig. 2 A). In the majority of species of grasses, however, the pales so closely invest the caryopsis that they become almost fused to the ovary wall (Fig. 1 E). In a few other cases the caryopsis, although enveloped by the pales, is not fused and easily separated, e.g. Timothy Grass (Fig. 26 c).

When ripe the rachis of the spikelet in grasses usually breaks off at a point near the base of the fruit. In those cases where

Fig. 1.—A. Inflorescence of Italian Rye-grass. B. Spikelet. C. Diagram of flowers on spikelet. D. Individual flower. E. Fruit or commercial seed.

1. Rachis; 2. outer glume; 3. awn; 4. outer pale; 5. inner pale; 6. rachilla; 7. ovary; 8. stigmas; 9. filament; 10. anthers; 11. lodicules.

the pales are present there is frequently attached to each fruit a portion of the rachis which supported the fruit immediately above. This little stalk-like structure is termed a " rachilla " (Fig. 1 E), and is often a useful diagnostic feature on the commercial seed. In a few instances, e.g. Yorkshire Fog (Fig. 21 B), the commercial seed consists of the entire spikelet with the glumes, pales and grains of one or more flowers attached.

The True Seed.—When a longitudinal section is cut the true seed may be examined (Fig. 2 A). This consists of a large proportion of starchy endosperm with a small embryo enclosed within a seed-coat or testa. The embryo is situated near the base of the seed, and is separated from the endosperm by a thin-walled shield-like structure, called the scutellum or cotyledon. It is composed of a short primary shoot (the plumule), a primary root (the radicle), and two pairs of secondary rootlets. Both plumule and radicle are enclosed within a sheath, which is continuous with the scutellum.

Germination.

When provided with an adequate supply of water and air, and with a suitable temperature the seeds begin to germinate. The endosperm is converted into simple sugars by an enzyme secreted by the scutellum, and transferred to the growing points of the young embryo. The young temporary rootlets then emerge through the sheath (*coleorhiza*) and assist in establishing the young seedling in the soil (Fig. 2 B). At the same time the plumule sheath (*coleoptile*) appears above the soil as a delicate, white tube-like structure. After a short time the temporary rootlets are replaced by permanent ones, which arise from the lowermost node of the stem, and the plumule pushes its first green leaf (Fig. 2 C, D, E) through a slit at the apex of the coleoptile. By this time practically the whole of the endosperm has been utilised by the embryo, and the plant is about to lead an independent existence.

FIG. 2.—A. Longitudinal section through caryopsis of Wheat. B. First stage in germination of Wheat. C. Second stage in germination of Wheat. D. Second stage in germination of Barley. E. Second stage in germination of Perennial Rye-grass. F. Third stage in germination of Wheat.
1. Ovary wall; 2. seed-coat; 3. scutellum; 4. endosperm; 5. plumule; 6. radicle; 7. secondary rootlets; 8. coleorhiza; 9. coleoptile; 10. permanent rootlets; 11. first green leaf; 12. first internode; 13. tillers; 14. leaf sheath; 15. leaf blade.

In fruits, such as wheat and rye, where the pales are absent, the roots and plumule emerge at the same point (Fig. 2 B). In Barley, Oats and the majority of grasses, however, where the pales remain attached, the plumule grows up beneath the pale and emerges at the opposite end to the young rootlets (Fig. 2 D, E).

A second stage of development is seen when more green leaves appear, and when the terminal bud finds its own level near the surface of the soil by an elongation of the first internode (Fig. 2 F). If the seed is sown too deeply the first internode elongates considerably and appears as a long wiry stem. In shallow sowing, the internodes are short and scarcely visible. Lateral buds are next formed in the axils of the leaves, which later break their way out from the enclosing leaf sheath to produce shoots or tillers. The tillering capacity of grasses varies in the different species and strains.

The Young Shoot.—This consists of a short stem upon which the young leaves are crowded and protected on the outside by a leaf sheath. Its shape, which varies from flattened to cylindrical, depends upon the degree of folding and rolling of the young leaf blades (Fig. 3 A, B, C).

The older stems of grasses which later bear inflorescences are usually cylindrical and hollow, except at the nodes which form the point of attachment of the leaves. If the stems grow up erect within their sheaths (intravaginal branching) a tufted habit of growth results (Fig. 8 D). If, on the other hand, the young shoots pierce through the sheaths in which they are enclosed (extravaginal branching) a straggly or spreading appearance is presented (Fig. 4 D).

In some species, stems other than the flowering ones may grow out horizontally to form stolons or rhizomes (Fig. 7 D). Such stoloniferous plants are able to propagate themselves rapidly on account of the adventitious roots produced at the nodes.

Leaves.—The leaves are arranged in two alternate rows on the stem (Fig. 3 D, E, F). Each leaf consists of two well-defined parts, (*a*) the sheath or lower portion attached to the stem at the nodes and surrounding the young leaves, and (*b*) the blade or upper portion which is free.

FIG. 3.—A. Section through young shoot of Italian Rye-grass showing rolled leaves and split sheath. B. Section through young shoot of Crested Dogstail showing folded leaves and split sheath. C. Section through young shoot of Cocksfoot showing shoot of folded leaves and entire sheath. D. Young shoot of Italian Rye-grass. E. Young Crested Dogstail. F. Young shoot of Cocksfoot.
1. Split leaf sheath; 2. auricles; 3. leaf blade; 4. ligule; 5. entire leaf sheath : 6. vascular bundles.

Leaf Sheath.—This is a tubular structure enclosing the lower-most portion of the stem, and may be either entire or split in the different species (Fig. 3 D, E, F). In many grasses a colouring pigment develops on the basal portion of the sheath, which may be either present over the entire surface or confined to the veins.

Leaf Blades.—The blades or laminæ are continuous with the upper portion of the leaf sheath. They may be either expanded, folded, rolled or solid and bristle-like (Figs. 6 E, 20 E, 7 E, 17 E). The presence or absence of ribs or veins running parallel from apex to base can usually be determined by the naked eye, but these are best studied from microscopical sections of the blade (Fig. 4 G).

In some species the veins are surrounded by thick-walled cells to form prominent ridges on the surface of the leaf blade (Fig. 16 G). In others, these ridges are small and inconspicuous (Fig. 15 G). There is, however, in the majority of cases a mid-rib on the under surface of the blade, when it is said to be keeled (Fig. 15 G).

A series of modified cells are always present, either at the base of each rib or flanking the mid-rib. These are known as motor cells, and can often be detected as transparent white lines when the blade is held up to the light (19 E).

The breadth, length and the degree of tapering of the apex of leaves vary in different grasses. The colour and hairiness of the blade often vary with age and habitat. In many cases the upper surface is dull, and the underside distinctly glossy and smooth.

Auricles.—The base of the leaf blade may be modified to form ledge-like processes on each side termed auricles (Fig. 3 D). They may be long and clasping the stem, or small and lobed.

Ligule.—At the junction between the leaf blade and sheath there is usually a small erect semi-transparent outgrowth called the ligule (Fig. 3 F). It may be long, short, serrated, blunt or pointed. Both the auricle and ligule characters are peculiar to, and constant in each species.

Root System.—When the young grass plant begins to unfold its leaves the primary rootlets of the embryo disappear, and are succeeded by adventitious roots which grow out from the lower-most nodes of the stem. These are usually numerous and very much branched, forming a dense tuft near the surface of the soil (Fig. 5 D). The length, fineness and colour of the roots vary slightly in different grasses.

CHAPTER 2

CHARACTERS WHICH INFLUENCE THE AGRICULTURAL VALUE OF GRASSES

GRASSES are generally classified as useful or useless by the farmer according to their particular value. Although there are over one hundred different types of British grasses, only about twenty are of any real agricultural value. The valuable grasses may, again be divided into groups according to different environments, and only a few types are sown in a seeds mixture to form a pasture in any one particular district.

In general, the value of a species will depend upon the following characteristics : (a) Productivity or yield, (b) Persistency, (c) Chemical composition, (d) Palatability, and (e) Winter greenness.

Productivity.

The weight of produce obtained from any one species will largely depend upon the length of the growing period and its tillering capacity. Perennial Rye-grass is said to be highly productive because it tillers freely and grows almost steadily from early spring until late autumn, whereas Tall Oat Grass, on the other hand, grows for a short period only and yields comparatively little bulk. Productivity is also influenced by the intensity of recovery after grazing or cutting, since these factors are more favourable to the growth of young tillers in some species than in others.

Persistency.

Grasses, such as Perennial Rye-grass, Cocksfoot and Timothy, live for a considerable number of years in a suitable environment, whereas Italian Rye-grass usually disappears after one or two seasons, irrespective of the surroundings. This indicates that before sowing seed mixtures for either temporary or permanent pastures, a study of the persistency of each species or strain is of the utmost importance.

Chemical Composition.

The value of a grass depends to a great extent upon the amount of proteins, minerals, fats and carbohydrates present. Recent research has proved that the leaves possess a higher percentage of proteins and minerals than the stems, and that a species with a high proportion of young leaves is extremely valuable from a feeding point of view. The majority of grasses become stemmy with age, but some types produce numerous stems early in life, which immediately renders them valueless to the farmer.

Palatability.

Although a species may be highly productive and persistent, with a satisfactory chemical composition, it may on account of its harsh or hairy leaves be unpalatable, and left unconsumed by stock, especially when in an advanced stage. Plants, such as Yorkshire Fog and Tall Fescue, are typical examples, which would otherwise be valuable components of seed mixtures.

Winter Greenness.

The value of a species will also largely depend upon its capacity to remain green during the winter months. Unfortunately most of the British grasses remain dormant, and leaf production is at a minimum during this period. Recent research has, however, indicated that young leys composed of indigenous strains remain greener and are far more productive in winter than old permanent pastures. Certain strains of Meadow Foxtail and Red Fescue have already been bred to yield a fair amount of leaf during February and March, and further work is in progress to produce winter green strains of different species to suit a wide range of conditions.

Plant Improvement.

Systematists and others have discovered that individual species varies according to the environment in which it grows. Perennial Rye-grass, for example, may in some districts appear tufted, stemmy and short lived, while in others a more persistent and leafy type exists. These, together with other differences, are nowadays used for classifying single species into varieties or strains, some of which possess a lower agricultural value than others.

Grass and clover seeds in this country have usually been obtained in the past from all parts of the world. Such a practice has often led to unsatisfactory results since the environment may be totally different, and unsuited for the growth of the particular variety or strain sown. Many New Zealand strains, however, do well in this country.

Recent work at the Welsh Plant Breeding Station has shown that commercial types are inferior to British wild or indigenous forms with regard to leafiness, persistency, productivity, winter greenness and other features. In consequence, indigenous forms of many species have been compared, and new types evolved by selection and hybridisation. Strains of indigenous Cocksfoot, Fescue, Timothy and Perennial Rye-grass have already been produced to suit different purposes and are at present sold by several British seed firms. New strains of Red and White Clover and Lucerne have also been produced. These new Aberystwyth strains are commonly called " S " strains ; a list of the more important ones are given below.

S.23.   Perennial Rye Grass—pasture type.
S.101. Perennial Rye Grass—pasture-hay type.
S.24.   Perennial Rye Grass—hay type.
S.143. Cocksfoot—pasture type.
S.26.   Cocksfoot—pasture-hay type.
S.37.   Cocksfoot—hay type.
S.50.   Timothy—extreme pasture type.
S.48.   Timothy—pasture-hay type.
S.51.   Timothy—hay type.
S.123. Red Clover (extra)—late flowering type.
S.151. Red Clover—medium early flowering type.
S.100. White Clover—very productive, large leaves.
S.184. Wild White Clover—improved strain.
S.53.   Meadow Fescue—pasture type.
S.215. Meadow Fescue—hay type.
S.58.   Sheep's Fescue—improved strain.
S.59.   Creeping Red Fescue—improved strain.
S.205. Lucerne—improved strain.

CHAPTER 3

KEY TO THE VEGETATIVE CHARACTERS OF SOME COMMON GRASSES

I. *Leaf needle-like* and not easily flattened out.

(Leaves of several grasses may assume needle-like form, but are easily unfolded or unrolled.)

A. Leaf distinctly folded (V section).

   (*a*) Ligule very short ; leaf delicate
                                 Festuca ovina et F. duriuscula.

   (*b*) Ligule prominent ; leaf hard, glaucous, upright ; roots wiry . . . . *Nardus stricta.*

B. Leaf practically solid, delicate (wheat grain section) ; roots red . . . . . . *Deschampsia flexuosa.*

II. *Leaf flat*, or if needle-like easily flattened out.

A. Leaf folded in bud ; shoot more or less flat.

   (*a*) Small claws at base of leaf ; basal sheaths smooth, shining pink ; ligule very short ; blade markedly ribbed above
                                 Lolium perenne.
   (Occasional plants have some tillers folded and some rolled.)

   (*b*) No claws at base of leaf.

     1. Aquatic grass with large leaves.

       (i) Sheath keeled ; blade yellowish-green, with yellow triangles at base ; prominently ribbed
                                Glyceria fluitans.
      (ii) Sheath not keeled ; blade not prominently ribbed ; plant reedy . . . . *Glyceria aquatica.*

     2. Plants not aquatic.

       (i) Leaf smooth, ribless, with two whitish median lines ; hooded tip.

(1) Leaf stiff, glaucous ; ligule very short (mountain limestone hills—in north and west)   .   *Sesleria*.

(2) Leaf not stiff, not glaucous.

    (a) Stem flattened ; ligule long ; blade shining below ; apex pointed ; plant usually tufted ; minute asperities on leaf sheath . *Poa trivialis*.

    (b) Stem rough ; ligule long ; blade dull underneath, often wrinkled transversely ; plant tufted (in flower all the year round) . . *Poa annua*.

    (c) Ligule short ; apex of blade blunt ; plant markedly stoloniferous ; no asperities on sheath *Poa pratensis*.

(Intermediate forms between *P. pratensis* and *P. trivialis* are common.)

    (ii) Leaf without median white lines.

    (1) Sheath or blade or both hairy.

        (a) Ligule long, membraneous ; sheath hirsute (hedge banks) . . . . . *Avena pubescens*.

        (b) Ligule a tuft of hairs ; long soft hairs sparsely scattered along edge and underside of leaf (poor and dry pastures) . . *Sieglingia decumbens*.

    (2) Sheath and blade smooth.

        (a) Seaside grass. Leaves hard, usually rolled up ; ligule long, bifid ; markedly stoloniferous *Ammophila arenaria*.

        (b) Stem very flat and sharp edged ; ligule long, plant tufted . . . *Dactylis glomerata*.

        (c) Leaves very harsh ; all ribs very prominent ; densely tufted ; no distinct mid-rib *Deschampsia caespitosa*.

        (d) Sheath below ground yellow ; blade short, trough-shaped and leathery (may appear rolled in bud) ; ligule short ; dead flowering stems generally present . . . . *Cynosurus cristatus*.

(e) Short leaves with rough edges and low ribs ; lower sheaths often reddish (poor pastures)

Briza media.

(f) Leaves rough, often rolled up ; alternate bands of green and mealy white on sheath (roadsides)

Avena pratensis.

B. Leaf rolled in bud ; stem cylindrical.

(a) Vertical peglike projection opposite base of blade ; stem square ; sheath hairy (woods)   .   . *Melica uniflora.*

(b) No peglike projection ; stem not square.

1. Claws at base of leaf.

(i) Sheath below ground smooth, shining pink ; ligule very short.

(a) Margin of blade smooth ; veins indistinct (hold up to light)   .   .   . *Lolium multiflorum.*

(b) Blade rougher, especially edges ; veins white (hold up to light) ; ligule rim-like

Festuca pratensis.

(c) Leaves larger, harsher (woods) *Bromus giganteus.*

(d) Annual (cornfield weed)   . *Lolium temulentum.* (*Agropyrum repens* may appear here also ; ligule reduced to a rim.)

(ii) Sheath below ground not smooth and not shining pink.

(1) Basal sheaths distinctly hairy.

(a) Hairs long, prominent ; ligule prominent ; blade large (woods)   .   . *Bromus asper et erectus.*

(b) Hairs short ; ligule very short ; blade thin, small (pastures)   .   .   .   . *Hordeum pratense.*

(c) Rim-like ligule   .   .   . *Agropyrum repens.*

(2) Basal sheaths smooth or nearly so.

(a) Large seaside grass. Leaves thick, glaucous, ridges prominent   .   .   . *Elymus arenarius.*

(b) Markedly stoloniferous ; ligule a mere rim ; blade shortly downy above (or occasionally smooth),

smooth below; basal sheaths often redden in
dry positions . . . *Agropyrum repens.*

(c) Ligule short; blade thin, papery, downy above
and below (roadsides and waste places)
Hordeum murinum.

(d) Annual cornfield weed; ligule very short
Lolium temulentum.

2. No claws at base of leaf.

(i) Lower sheaths hairy.

(1) A few long hairs around ligule, otherwise smooth;
characteristic smell and taste
Anthoxanthum odoratum.

(2) Basal sheaths white with pink veins.
   a. Tufted . . . . . *Holcus lanatus.*

   aa. Rhizomes . . . . *Holcus mollis.*

(3) Basal sheaths uniformly hairy and not with pink
veins.

   †. Ligule prominent, membraneous.

   A. Sheath keeled; leaves thin, papery, hirsute.

   (a) Leaves light green, covered with long hairs,
   rather thinly scattered (woods)
   Brachypodium sylvaticum.

   (b) Leaves downy above and below; hairs
   short; ribs indistinct (waste places and
   cornfields) . . . *Bromus mollis.*

   (c) Leaves not so densely downy; hairs longer;
   upper sheaths smooth (waste places); easily
   develops red colour . . *Bromus sterilis.*

   B. Sheath not keeled, leaves not papery, light
   green . . . . *Trisetum flavescens.*

   ††. Ligule inconspicuous.

   (a) Sheath and upper surface of blade sparsely
   covered with long white hairs; blade stiff
   and pointed (moors) . *Molinia caerulea.*

    (b) Sheath and blade hirsute ; blade narrow. often inrolled ; ligule a yellow jagged line (dry pastures) . . . *Koeleria cristata.*

(ii) Sheaths smooth or nearly so.

  (1) Aquatics with large leaves.

    (a) Ligule a tuft of hairs ; leaves 9″-18″ long, stiff, ribs marked . . . *Phragmites* (*Arundo*).

    (b) Ligule membraneous ; leaves smaller ; ribs low
                                    Digraphis arundinacea.

  (2) Plants not aquatic.

    (*i*) Wood grass ; leaves large, light green, ligule large . . . . . *Milium effusum.*

    (*ii*) Meadow and pasture grasses.

    A. Marked colour in old basal sheaths below ground.

    (a) Sheath below ground dark brown, violet-brown or nearly black ; blade large, markedly ribbed . . . *Alopecurus pratensis.*

    (b) Sheath below ground yellow (leaf really folded in bud) ; dead flowering stems usually present . . . *Cynosurus cristatus.*

    B. Old sheaths below ground not markedly coloured (but Timothy often bright brown in outer old sheaths).

  (x) Leaf more or less prominently ribbed.

  α. Perennial.

    (a) Stem bent at nodes ; blade short, not keeled ; sharply ribbed ; bluish-green (wet places)
                                  Alopecurus geniculatus.

    (b) Leaves very pointed and taped-based ; frequently has long stolons (cornfields, pastures, waste places). Very short hairs on back of ligule (hold to light and use lens). On drying, leaves become dark grey-green. Important distinctions from Phleum
                                  Agrostis spp.

  β. Annual cornfield weed ; upright tufts
                                  Alopecurus agrestis.

(xx) Ribs low and inconspicuous ; stem often swollen at base.

   (a) Sheath prominently keeled ; leaves dark green with a bitter taste ; often sparsely hairy ; lower outer leaf bases often purple-red   *Arrhenatherum avenaceum et bulbosum.*

   (b) Sheath scarcely keeled, except at top ; leaves light green, sweet taste ; upright habit when young ; white at base ; ligule without hairs ; dries to silvery-grey colour ; often closely resembles A. grostis

Phleum pratense.

CHAPTER 4

BOTANICAL DESCRIPTIONS OF GRASSES

Couch Grass (*Agropyrum repens*)

A. *Floral organs.*

Time of flowering—Mid and late summer.

Inflorescence—Spikate, erect, 2 to 6 inches long, culms 1 to 3 feet high.

Spikelets—Sessile on main axis, arranged on alternate sides ; 8 to 10 in number ; side of spikelet flat on rachis ; 4 to 6 flowers.

Glumes—Two, almost equal, narrow, stiff, pointed.

Pales—Two, outer one may or may not possess a short awn ; rachilla prominent.

Commercial seed—Single grain plus pales, plus rachilla.

B. *Vegetative organs.*

Habit of growth—Creeping perennial, with long stout rhizomes.

Root system—Fibrous, tufts of fibrous roots at nodes on rhizomes.

Shoots—Rounded.

Leaf sheath—Split, hairy, often red in dry places.

Leaf blade—Very pointed, downy above (or occasionally smooth), smooth below or slightly hairy ; slightly ribbed above.

Auricles—Prominent.

Ligule—Short, blunt.

C. *Distribution.*

Indigenous to Europe, Asia, America, and from Mediterranean to Arctic regions. Common in Britain on arable land.

D. *Economic value.*

A troublesome weed on most arable land.

FIG. 4.—A. Inflorescence. B. Spikelet. C. Commercial seed. D. Vegetative organs. E. Outline of leaf blade. F. Junction of leaf sheath and blade. G. Section through leaf blade.

A

B ×4·6

C ×6

D

F

G

E

Brown top, Creeping, or Common Bent (Agrostis tenuis)

A. *Floral organs.*

Time of flowering—Summer and early autumn.

Inflorescence—Panicle, erect, elegant, slender branches, spreading during time of flowering ; dark brown in colour when matured.

Spikelets—Numerous, small, one-flowered ; stalks vary in length.

Glumes—Two, almost equal in size, slightly keeled.

Pales—Two, awnless, a small tuft of hairs at base.

Commercial seed—Very small, composed of the two pales enclosing a small ovoid grain.

B. *Vegetative organs.*

Habit of growth—Varies from a dense tuft in dry places to a creeping perennial in richer soil.

Root system—Fibrous, fine, yellowish-brown.

Shoots—Rounded, glabrous.

Leaf sheath—Split.

Leaf blade—Rolled in the shoot, distinctly ribbed above ; long, narrow and finely pointed ; on drying becoming dark greyish-green.

Auricles—Absent.

Ligule—Short and blunt ; sometimes short hairs on back of ligule.

C. *Distribution.*

Indigenous to Europe, Asia and North America. Most common on dry light soils.

D. *Economic value.*

Nutritive value and palatability low. Productivity low. Not sown in seeds mixtures, except for the formation of lawns and greens.

Fig. 5.—A. Inflorescence. B. Spikelet. C. Commercial seed. D. Vegetative organs. E. Outline of leaf blade. F. Junction of leaf sheath and blade. G. Section through leaf blade.

A

B
X 16·6

C
X 20

F

G

D

E

Meadow Foxtail (*Alopecurus pratensis*)

A. *Floral organs.*

Time of flowering—Spring and early summer.
Inflorescence—Cylindrical spike-like panicle, fairly compact and soft, 1 to 4 inches long ; culms 1 to 3 feet high.
Spikelets—Numerous, one-flowered, short stalks, flat.
Glumes—Two, equal length, boat-shaped, prominent keel with short hairs along edge.
Pales—Only outer one present, bearing slender basal awn.
Commercial seed—One complete spikelet.

B. *Vegetative organs.*

Habit of growth—Tufted perennial, slightly creeping.
Root system—Fibrous, yellow, sometimes short stolons.
Shoots—Rounded, glabrous.
Leaf sheath—Split, brown in colour, older ones very dark brown, glabrous.
Leaf blade—Dark green, large, flat, distinctly ribbed, glabrous.
Auricles—Absent.
Ligule—Small, blunt.

C. *Distribution.*

Indigenous to temperate and colder regions of Northern and Southern hemispheres. Most common in Britain on rich fertile heavy soils.

D. *Economic value.*

Nutritive value and palatability extremely high. Productivity of some indigenous strains high throughout growing season. Very leafy in early spring and very winter green. Seed expensive and difficult to establish. Not normally recommended for seeds mixtures.

FIG. 6.—A. Inflorescence. B. Spikelet and commercial seed. D. Vegetative organs. E. Outline of leaf blade. F. Junction of leaf sheath and blade. G. Section through leaf blade.

A

B ×12

D

E

F

G

Marram Grass (*Ammophila arenaria*)

A. *Floral organs.*

Time of flowering—July.

Inflorescence—Panicle, erect, close, appearing as a cylindrical spike, 5 to 6 inches long ; culms 1 to 3 feet high.

Spikelets—Crowded, long, narrow, containing one flower.

Glumes—Two, unequal, stiff.

Pales—Two, stiff, tuft of hairs on base.

Commercial seed—Single grain plus pales.

B. *Vegetative organs.*

Habit of growth—Creeping perennial.

Root system—Fibrous, rooting at nodes on rhizomes.

Shoots—Rounded.

Leaf sheath—Split.

Leaf blade—Rolled in shoot, erect, hard, narrow, usually rolled, very pointed, prominent ribs on upper surface, unequal, hairs on upper surface.

Auricles—Absent.

Ligule—Long, bifid.

C. *Distribution.*

Indigenous on coasts of Europe and North America. Common in Britain on sand dunes.

D. *Economic value.*

No agricultural value. Used for sand binding, and mat making.

Fig. 7.—A. Inflorescence. B. Spikelet. C. Commercial seed. D. Vegetative organs. E. Outline of leaf blade. F. Junction of leaf sheath and blade. G. Section through leaf blade.

×5·3

C

A

×4

B

D

F

E

G

3

Sweet Vernal (Anthoxanthum odoratum)

A. *Floral organs.*

Time of flowering—Spring and early summer.

Inflorescence—Cylindrical spike-like panicle, 1 to 3 inches long ; culms 1 to 2 feet high.

Spikelets—Numerous, one-flowered, short stalks.

Glumes—Two pairs ; outer pair unequal, pointed but not awned, green when young but yellow when matured ; inner pair shorter than outer ones, hairy, and rich brown when ripe. Lower inner glume with small dorsal awn ; outer glume with basal awn longer than itself, twisted and bent near top of glume.

Pales—Two, brown, enclosing caryopsis ; two stamens per floret.

Commercial seed—Single grain, plus pales, plus innermost pair of glumes.

B. *Vegetative organs.*

Habit of growth—Tufted.

Root system—Fibrous, short, yellowish-brown.

Shoots—Rounded, often glabrous.

Leaf sheath—Split, slightly hairy.

Leaf blade—Fairly dark green, pointed, slightly hairy, faintly ribbed on upper surface ; characteristic smell and taste.

Auricles—Absent, replaced by small tufts of hairs.

Ligule—Prominent, white.

C. *Distribution.*

Indigenous to Europe, Asia and America, and from Mediterranean to Arctic regions. Most common in Britain in southern counties. Found on all types of soil in lowlands.

D. *Economic value.*

Nutritive value low, and not recommended for including in seeds mixtures.

Fig. 8.—A. Inflorescence. B. Spikelet. C. Commercial seed. C_1. Seed with inner glumes removed. D. Vegetative organs. E. Outline of leaf blade. F. Junction of leaf sheath and blade. G. Section through leaf blade.

A

C

×10

C₁   ×16·6

B   ×8

D

F

G

E

Tall Oat Grass (*Arrhenatherum avenaceum*)

A. *Floral organs.*

Time of flowering—June and July.

Inflorescence—Panicle narrow, loose, 6 to 8 inches long; spreading only when flowers are open; culms 2 to 3 feet high.

Spikelets—Numerous, two flowers, the upper one perfect, the lower one staminate.

Glumes—Two, thin, pointed, unequal.

Pales—Two per floret; dorsal, twisted and bent awn on outer pale of lower flower; outer pale of upper flower possesses a minute sub-terminal awn; hairs at base.

Commercial seed—Complete spikelet minus pair of glumes.

B. *Vegetative organs.*

Habit of growth—Loose, tufted perennial.

Root system—Fibrous, long, deep yellow.

Shoots—Rounded, older stems often with swollen nodes at base (A. bulbosum).

Leaf sheath—Split, sparsely hairy, older ones often purple red.

Leaf blade—Dark green, bitter taste, rolled in shoot, keeled, slightly hairy on upper surface, ribs on upper surface low; long, narrow, pointed.

Auricles—Absent.

Ligule—Blunt; variable in size.

C. *Distribution.*

Indigenous to Europe, Western Asia and North America. Most common in Britain on hedgerows and light soils.

D. *Economic value.*

Proportion of leaf stem low. Cannot stand up to grazing, but produces heavy hay crop on light land. Its inclusion in seeds mixtures can only be justified under these conditions.

Fig. 9.—A. Inflorescence. B. Spikelet. C. Commercial seed. D. Vegetative organs. E. Outline of leaf blade. F. Junction of leaf sheath and blade. G. Section through leaf blade.

Perennial Oat Grass (*Avena pratensis*)

A. *Floral organs.*

Time of flowering—June and July.

Inflorescence—Panicle erect, almost reduced to a simple raceme ; 1 to 1½ feet high.

Spikelets—Erect, shining, large, 3 to 5 flowered.

Glumes—Two, unequal, pointed, keeled.

Pales—Two, outer one white, slightly cleft at apex, with a dorsal twisted awn ; awn bent, pales hairy at base.

Commercial seed—Single grain plus pales, plus rachilla ; rachilla round, long, hairy.

B. *Vegetative organs.*

Habit of growth—Erect perennial, sometimes slightly creeping.

Root system—Fibrous, yellowish-brown.

Shoots—Flat.

Leaf sheath—Split, usually glabrous, alternate bands of white and green.

Leaf blade—Folded in shoot, rough, often rolled up ; keeled below, almost ribless above ; glabrous. Sometimes slightly hairy.

Auricles—Absent.

Ligule—Fairly prominent.

C. *Distribution.*

Indigenous to Europe and Asia. Most common in Britain on Cotswolds.

D. *Economic value.*

Nutritive value low, used for rough grazing on dry, chalky soils.

Fig. 10.—A. Inflorescence. B. Spikelet. C. Commercial seed. D. Vegetative organs. E. Outline of leaf blade. F. Junction of leaf sheath and blade. G. Section through leaf blade.

A

F

D

C

B

×4·6

×3·3

G

E

Heath False Brome (*Brachypodium pinnatum*)

A. *Floral organs.*

Time of flowering—June and July.
Inflorescence—Almost spikate, erect, culm 1 to 3 feet high.
Spikelets—Erect, long, 8 to 16 florets.
Glumes—Two, unequal, pointed, slightly hairy.
Pales—Two, outer pale with short terminal awn, slightly hairy.
Commercial seed—Single grain plus two pales, plus rachilla.

B. *Vegetable Organs.*

Habit of growth—Tufted perennial, creeping.
Root system—Fibrous, yellow.
Shoots—Rounded.
Leaf sheath—Split, hairy.
Leaf blade—Rolled in shoot, light green, stiff, erect, slightly hairy ; tendency to roll inwards.
Auricles—Absent.
Ligule—Long, prominent.

C. *Distribution.*

Indigenous to Europe and Asia. Most common in Britain in southern and eastern districts in broken down pastures.

D. *Economic value.*

Nutritive value low, not recommended for sowing in seeds mixtures.

Fig. 11.—A. Inflorescence. B. Spikelet. C. Commercial seed. D. Vegetative organs. E. Outline of leaf blade. F. Junction of leaf sheath and blade. G. Section through leaf blade.

A

B

×2·6

C

×5·3

D

E

F

G

Wood False Brome Grass (Brachypodium sylvaticum)

A. *Floral organs.*

Time of flowering—June and July.
Inflorescence—Almost spikate, culms 1 to 3 feet high.
Spikelets—Long, almost drooping, about 1 inch long, 8 to
16 florets.
Glumes—Two, unequal, slightly hairy, pointed.
Pales—Two, outer one awned, inner one hairy along edges.
Commercial seed—Complete grain plus two pales, plus
rachilla.

B. *Vegetative organs.*

Habit of growth—Tufted perennial, slightly creeping.
Root system—Fibrous, yellow.
Shoots—Rounded.
Leaf sheath—Split, hairy.
Leaf blade—Rolled in shoot, light green, long, very pointed,
both surfaces sparsely covered with long hairs, slightly
keeled below.
Auricles—Absent.
Ligule—Prominent, blunt, slightly serrated.

C. *Distribution.*

Indigenous to Europe and Asia, and most common in Britain
in woods and shady places.

D. *Economic value.*

Nutritive value low, not sown in seeds mixtures.

Fig. 12.—A. Inflorescence. B. Spikelet. C. Commercial seed. D. Vegetative organs. E. Outline of leaf blade. F. Junction of leaf sheath
and blade. G. Section through leaf blade.

Soft Brome Grass (*Bromus mollis*)

A. *Floral organs*.

Time of flowering—May and June.

Inflorescence—Panicle erect, compact, 6 to 8 inches long ; culms 1 to 2 feet high.

Spikelets—Fairly numerous, 8 to 10 florets, broad at base, becoming pointed.

Glumes—Two, hairy, unequal ; outer glume reaching to about one-third way up spikelet.

Pales—Two, hairy ; outer pale broad, bifid apex, subterminal awn ; inner pale thin. Rachilla bent.

Commercial seed—One single grain plus pales, plus rachilla.

B. *Vegetative organs*.

Habit of growth—A tufted biennial, not very persistent.

Root system—Fibrous, yellowish-brown.

Shoots—Rounded.

Leaf sheath—Entire, hairy, striated.

Leaf blade—Hairy above and below ; pointed, ribs almost indistinct.

Auricles—Absent.

Ligule—Short, serrated.

C. *Distribution*.

Indigenous to Europe and Asia. Common in Britain in open waste places and cornfields, often in hayland on sandy soils.

D. *Economic value*.

Nutritive value and palatability low.

Fig. 13.—A. Inflorescence. B. Spikelet. C. Commercial seed. D. Vegetative organs. E. Outline of leaf blade. F. Junction of leaf sheath and blade. G. Section through leaf blade

A

B ×2·3

C ×4·6

D

E

F

G

Crested Dogstail (*Cynosurus cristatus*)

A. *Floral organs.*

Time of flowering—June and July.

Inflorescence—One-sided spikelike panicle, erect, 1 to 3 inches long ; culm stiff, wiry when old, approximately 1 foot high.

Spikelets—Numerous, in almost sessile clusters arranged on one side of the axis ; the outer spikelet of the cluster sterile, the inner one fertile containing 3 to 5 florets.

Glumes—Two per spikelet, equal in size in both empty and flowering spikelets ; keeled, short awn, pointed.

Pales—Two, usually a bright yellow colour, especially towards the base ; rachilla cylindrical, prominent, capped.

Commercial seed—Single grain plus pales, plus rachilla.

B. *Vegetative organs.*

Habit of growth—Dense, tufted perennial.

Root system—Fibrous, yellowish-brown.

Shoots—Rounded, glabrous.

Leaf sheath—Split, yellow below ground when old, glabrous.

Leaf blade—Rolled in shoot, dark green, short, leathery ; trough-shaped near base, ribbed above, glossy below, glabrous.

Auricles—Absent.

Ligule—Very short, blunt.

C. *Distribution.*

Indigenous to Europe, Asia and America. Common on poor dry soils, and also on rich soils.

D. *Economic value.*

Nutritive value and palatability high. Productivity highest during late summer. Rapidly develops wiry flowering stems, which are unattractive to stock. Very winter green and valuable as a bottom grass on upland pastures and poor dry soils.

Fig. 14.—A. Inflorescence.   B. Fertile spikelet.   B₁. Sterile spikelet. C. Commercial seed.   D. Vegetative organs.   E. Outline of leaf blade. F. Junction of leaf sheath and blade.   G. Section through leaf blade.

A

D

C ×8

B ×6.6

B₁ ×5.3

E

F

G

Cocksfoot (*Dactylis glomerata*)

A. *Floral organs.*

Time of flowering—May and June.

Inflorescence—Panicle erect, flowering stalks 2 to 3 feet high.

Spikelets—Arranged in dense clusters on short stiff branches, 2 to 3 flowers per spikelet.

Glumes—Two glumes almost equal, distinctly keeled and pointed, rough edges, slightly hairy.

Pales—Two, outer pale with curved point keeled from top to bottom, inner one membranous ; rachilla cylindrical and prominent, capped.

Commercial seed—Consists of grain plus pales, frequently two or three seeds attached.

B. *Vegetative organs.*

Habit of growth—Densely tufted perennial.

Root system—Fibrous, yellowish-brown.

Shoots—Flat.

Leaf sheath—Entire, glabrous, keeled.

Leaf blade—Folded in shoot, light green, glabrous, rough edges, ribless above, keeled below ; pointed.

Auricles—Absent.

Ligule—Long, membraneous, conspicuous.

C. *Distribution.*

Indigenous to Europe, Asia and Africa. Most common in Britain on heavy, fertile soils in meadows and waste places.

D. *Economic value.*

Nutritive value high, and very palatable in young stage. Productivity high. Starts growth early in spring, and recovers quickly in the aftermath. Recommended for seeds mixtures for both temporary and permanent pastures. Pedigree leafy strains are available to suit different purposes. The " mop " types are suitable for grazing, and the taller leafy types for hay. There are also intermediate types.

Fig. 15.—A. Inflorescence. B. Spikelet. C. Commercial seed. D. Vegetative organs. E. Outline of leaf blade. F. Junction of leaf sheath and blade. G. Section through leaf blade.

×6·6

×6·6

4

Tufted Hair Grass (Deschampsia caespitosa)

A. *Floral organs.*

Time of flowering—July and August.

Inflorescence—Panicle, spreading slender branches, sometimes 1 foot long ; culms 2 to 4 feet high.

Spikelets—Numerous, 2 to 3 flowers per spikelet ; purplish or silvery-grey in colour.

Glumes—Two, unequal, long and pointed.

Pales—Two, outer pale serrated at apex with fine awn inserted near its base ; not so long as the pale itself ; tuft of hairs at base.

Commercial seed—Single grain plus pale, plus rachilla. Rachilla long, hairy.

B. *Vegetative organs.*

Habit of growth—A tall densely, tufted perennial.

Root system—Very fibrous, yellowish-brown.

Shoots—Rounded, glabrous.

Leaf sheath—Split, slightly keeled, glabrous.

Leaf blade—Dark green, very harsh, ribs on upper surface equal and very prominent ; no distinct mid-rib, pointed ; glabrous.

Auricles—Absent.

Ligule—Long, whitish, acute.

C. *Distribution.*

Indigenous to Europe, and from Mediterranean to Arctic regions. Common in Britain in moist, shady places.

D. *Economic value.*

Nutritive value low, a weed in wet shady places.

FIG. 16.—A. Inflorescence. B. Spikelet. C. Commercial seed. D. Vegetative organs. E. Outline of leaf blade. F. Junction of leaf sheath and blade. G. Section through leaf blade.

A

C

×26·6

D

B

×13·3

F

E

G

Wavy Hair Grass (*Deschampsia flexuosa*)

A. *Floral organs.*

Time of flowering—July.

Inflorescence—Spreading panicle erect, 2 to 3 inches long ; culms 1 to 1½ feet high.

Spikelets—Numerous, two flowers, shiny.

Glumes—Two, unequal, pointed.

Pales—Two, outer one notched at apex with basal awn ; awn twisted, longer than pale and bent half-way ; minute hairs near base.

Commercial seed—Single grain plus pales, plus rachilla.

B. *Vegetative organs.*

Habit of growth—Tufted perennial.

Root system—Very fibrous, reddish in colour.

Shoots—Rounded, glabrous.

Leaf sheath—Split, glabrous.

Leaf blade—Dark green, needle-like ; edges rolled inwards, practically solid, glabrous.

Auricles—Absent.

Ligule—Short, broad.

C. *Distribution.*

Indigenous to Europe, Asia, North America and Chile. Common in Britain on heaths and hilly pastures.

D. *Economic value.*

Nutritive value low and not sown in seeds mixtures.

Fig. 17.—A. Inflorescence. B. Spikelet. C. Commercial seed. D. Vegetative organs. E. Outline of leaf blade. F. Junction of leaf sheath and blade. G. Section through leaf blade.

×8.6

C

A

×6.6

B

D

E

G

F

Sheep's Fescue (*Festuca ovina*)

A. *Floral organs.*

Time of flowering—May and June.

Inflorescence—Panicle compact, 2 to 4 inches long, culms 1 to 2 feet high.

Spikelets—5 to 8 florets.

Glumes—Two, unequal, slightly hairy.

Pales—Two, outer pale glabrous or hairy, short awn point ; rachilla round, prominent.

Commercial seed—Complete grain plus pales, plus rachilla.

B. *Vegetative organs.*

Habit of growth—Tufted perennial, dense.

Root system—Very fibrous, yellowish-brown.

Shoots—Cylindrical.

Leaf sheath—Split.

Leaf blade—Folded in shoot, dark green, radical leaves, permanently folded, needle-like, glabrous, delicate, stem leaves open and flat.

Auricles—Small, erect.

Ligule—Very small, often absent.

C. *Distribution.*

Indigenous to Europe, Asia, North America, and from Mediterranean to the Arctic regions. Most common in Britain in hilly pastures and in open dry places.

D. *Economic value.*

Nutritive value and palatability moderately high. Productivity low. Hardy and drought resistant. Useful grass on poor upland pastures. Not usually recommended for inclusion in seeds mixtures.

FIG. 18.—A. Inflorescence. B. Spikelet. C. Commercial seed. D. Vegetative organs. E. Outline of leaf blade. F. Junction of leaf sheath and blade. G. Section through leaf blade.

A

C ×20

D

E

F

B ×10·6

G

Meadow Fescue (*Festuca pratensis*)

A. *Floral organs.*

Time of flowering—June and July.
Inflorescence—Panicle, with secondary branches large ;
culms 1 to 2 feet high.
Spikelets—5 to 10 flowers.
Glumes—Two, unequal, outer one large and pointed.
Pales—Two, outer pale slightly awned or very pointed ;
rachilla cylindrical, capped, outstanding.
Commercial seed—One single grain, plus pales and rachilla.

B. *Vegetative organs.*

Habit of growth—Tufted perennial.
Root system—Fibrous, yellowish-brown.
Shoots—Rounded.
Leaf sheath—Split, reddish colour around basal parts ;
glabrous.
Leaf blade—Rolled in shoot, dark green, distinct ribs above,
lower surface smooth, glossy ; keeled ; edges harsh when
old ; distinct white longitudinal lines when held to light.
Auricles—Small if present.
Ligule—Small, rim-like, blunt.

C. *Distribution.*

Indigenous to Europe, Asia and North America. Most common in Britain on rich, heavy, moist pastures, especially when soil is rich in lime.

D. *Economic value.*

Nutritive value high. Palatability decreases with age. High proportion of leaf to stem. Recommended in seeds mixtures for permanent leys on suitable soils.

Fig. 19.—A. Inflorescence. B. Spikelet. C. Commercial seed. D. Vegetative organs. E. Outline of leaf blade. F. Junction of leaf sheath and blade. G. Section through leaf blade.

A

D

C ×8·6

B ×4

F

E

G

Red Fescue (*Festuca rubra*)

A. *Floral organs.*

Time of flowering—June and July.

Inflorescence—Panicle, compact, 2 to 4 inches long, culms 1 to 2 feet high ; erect, reddish when ripe.

Spikelets—5 to 8 florets.

Glumes—Two, unequal, may be slightly hairy.

Pales—Two, outer pale usually red ; awn point short but may vary in length ; rachilla round.

Commercial seed—One single grain plus pales and rachilla.

B. *Vegetative organs.*

Habit of growth—Tufted perennial, may sometimes be slightly creeping.

Root system—Fibrous, yellowish-brown.

Shoots—Rounded to oval.

Leaf sheath—Mostly entire, sometimes slightly hairy.

Leaf blade—Folded in shoot ; dark green ; stem leaves flat, other leaves mostly folded and needlelike. Usually a few scattered hairs.

Auricles—Small.

Ligule—Minute, often absent.

C. *Distribution.*

Indigenous to Europe, Asia, North America, and from Mediterranean to Arctic regions. Most common in Britain in hilly pastures.

D. *Economic value.*

Nutritive value and palatability high. When young, indigenous strains are productive and often remain green in winter. On good soils it tends to suppress the white clover.

FIG. 20.—A. Inflorescence. B. Spikelet. C. Commercial seed. D. Vegetative organs. E. Outline of leaf blade. F. Junction of leaf sheath and blade. G. Section through leaf blade.

A

B   ×6

C   ×10

D

E

F

G

Yorkshire Fog (Holcus lanatus)

A. *Floral organs.*

Time of flowering—June and July.

Inflorescence—Panicle, 2 to 3 inches long ; close green and compact when young, open and spreading later ; pinkish in colour.

Spikelets—Numerous, two flowers ; the lower flower perfect, the upper one staminate.

Glumes—Two, hairy, unequal, the outer one broad with a short awn point ; keeled.

Pales—Two, outer pale of lower flower awnless, shiny, and the outer pale of the upper flower with a sub-terminal fish hook awn, becoming curved when older.

Commercial seed—Usually the complete spikelet.

B. *Vegetative organs.*

Habit of growth—Tufted, sometimes slightly creeping.

Root system—Yellowish-brown.

Shoots—Round.

Leaf sheath—Split, hairy ; basal sheaths white with pink longitudinal veins.

Leaf blade—Lightish-green, hairy, rolled in shoot.

Auricles—Absent.

Ligule—Prominent, serrated, membraneous, hairy.

C. *Distribution.*

Indigenous to Europe and Asia. Most common in Britain in moist meadows and waste places.

D. *Economic value.*

Palatability low, indigenous strains sometimes recommended for seeds mixtures for improving upland pastures.

Fig. 21.—A. Inflorescence. B. Spikelet. C_1. Upper and lower florets. D. Vegetative organs. E. Outline of leaf blade. F. Junction of leaf sheath and blade. G. Section through leaf blade.

A

C₁

×11·3

B

×10·6

D

E

F

G

Italian Rye-Grass (*Lolium multiflorum*)

A. *Floral organs.*

Time of flowering—May or June.

Inflorescence—Spikate, erect, 1 to 2 feet high.

Spikelets—3 to 10 florets, alternating in two rows on rachis, edge on to rachis.

Glumes—Inner glume absent ; outer glume shorter than spikelet.

Pales—Outer pale smooth, with distinct terminal awn.

Commercial seed—Single grain plus pales, plus rachilla. Rachilla flat to rounded.

B. *Vegetative organs.*

Habit of growth—Tufted, dense.

Root system—Fibrous, yellowish-brown.

Shoots—Rounded, glabrous.

Leaf sheath—Split, reddish colour below, glabrous.

Leaf blade—Dark green, margin smooth, glossy below, dull above, distinctly ribbed ; blades rolled in shoot, glabrous.

Auricles—Prominent when old.

Ligule—Small, blunt.

C. *Distribution.*

Cultivated strains in temperate regions. Not indigenous to Britain.

D. *Economic value.*

Nutritive value and palatability high. Productivity high during spring and autumn months. Persists for two years only. Sown in seeds mixtures for temporary leys. Useful for early spring bite and catch cropping. Sometimes used as a nurse crop in direct re-seeding.

Fig. 22.—A. Inflorescence.   B. Spikelet.   C. Commercial seed.   D. Vegetative organs.   E. Outline of leaf blade.   F. Junction of leaf sheath and blade.   G. Section through leaf blade.

A

B ×4

C ×5·3

D

E

F

G

Perennial Rye-Grass (*Lolium perenne*)

A. *Floral organs.*

Time of flowering—June, with considerable variation according to strain and other factors.

Inflorescence—Spikate, erect, 1 to 2 feet high.

Spikelets—Sessile 3 to 10 florets, alternating in two rows, edge on to rachis.

Glumes—Inner glume absent ; outer glume shorter than spikelet.

Pales—Outer pale smooth ; awnless, rachilla oval in section. No cap.

Commercial seed—Single grain plus pales. Barge shape, rachilla flat, elliptical in section.

B. *Vegetative organs.*

Habit of growth—Tufted.

Root system—Fibrous, yellowish-brown.

Shoots—Flattened, glabrous.

Leaf sheath—Entire or split, reddish colour below, glabrous.

Leaf blade—Dark green, glossy below, dull above, distinctly ribbed. Leaf blades folded in shoot ; glabrous.

Auricles—Small if present.

Ligule—Small, blunt.

C. *Distribution.*

Indigenous to fertile soils in Britain, Europe and Asia. Uncommon on moorlands and upland pastures.

D. *Economic value.*

Nutritive value and palatability high. Productivity high throughout growing season and persists over a number of years. Both commercial and indigenous strains sown in seeds mixtures for permanent and temporary leys. Pedigree strains are available to suit different purposes, such as grazing, hay and intermediate types.

Fig. 23.—A. Inflorescence. B. Spikelet. C. Commercial seed. D. Vegetative organs. E. Outline of leaf blade. F. Junction of leaf sheath and blade. G. Section through leaf blade.

A   B ×3·3   C ×6·3   E   D   F   G

Flying Bent (*Molinia caerulea*)

A. *Floral organs.*

Time of flowering—July and August.

Inflorescence—Panicle narrow, 6 inches long, green to purplish, branches arise in alternate tufts on the culm; culm swollen at base.

Spikelets—Numerous, small, narrow, pointed, 2 to 3 flowers.

Glumes—Two, unequal, acute, shorter than pales.

Pales—Two, purple, open at top ; rachilla rounded, swollen near tip.

Commercial seed—Single grain plus pales, plus rachilla.

B. *Vegetative organs.*

Habit of growth—Stiff coarse perennial tufts.

Root system—Fibrous, tough, cord-like, yellowish-brown.

Shoots—Rounded.

Leaf sheath—Split, slightly hairy.

Leaf blade—Long, narrow, flat, stiff ; rolled in shoot, very pointed ; upper surface sparseley covered with long white hairs.

Auricles—Absent.

Ligule—Inconspicuous, represented by presence of hairs.

C. *Distribution.*

Indigenous to Europe and Asia, and from Mediterranean to Arctic regions. Most common in Britain on wet heaths, upland moors, woods and waste places.

D. *Economic value.*

Nutritive value, low, not sown in seeds mixtures.

FIG. 24.—A. Inflorescence.   B. Spikelet.   C. Commercial seed.   D. Vegetative organs.   E. Outline of leaf blade.   F. Junction of leaf sheath and blade.   G. Section through leaf blade.

Moor Mat Grass (*Nardus stricta*)

A. *Floral organs.*

Time of flowering—July.

Inflorescence—Spike, erect, culms 1 to 2 feet high.

Spikelets—Arranged on one side of rachis ; sessile, one flowered ; often purplish in colour.

Glumes—Absent.

Pales—Two, outer one narrow and ending in a fine awn point.

Commercial seed—Single grain plus pales.

B. *Vegetative organs.*

Habit of growth—Dense, tufted perennial.

Root system—Tough and wiry, yellowish.

Shoots—Round.

Leaf sheath—Split.

Leaf blade—Hard, glaucous, upright, permanently folded, 5 ribs on upper surface.

Auricles—Absent.

Ligule—Small and blunt, thick.

C. *Distribution.*

Indigenous to Europe and Asia. Most common in Britain on dry upland pastures and moors.

D. *Economic value.*

Nutritive value low, not recommended for sowing in seeds mixtures.

Fig. 25.—A. Inflorescence. B. Spikelet. C. Commercial seed. D. Vegetative organs. E. Outline of leaf blade. F. Junction of leaf sheath and blade. G. Section through leaf blade.

Timothy (*Phleum pratense*)

A. *Floral organs.*

Time of flowering—July and August.

Inflorescence—Cylindrical compact spike-like panicle, 1 to 6 inches long ; culms 1 to 2½ feet high.

Spikelets—Numerous, one-flowered, very short stalks.

Glumes—Two, equal length, broad, slightly hairy ; keeled, terminating in rough awn points ; awns shorter than glumes ; short stiff hairs along edges of keel.

Pales—Two, thin, silvery-white.

Commercial seed—Ovoid in shape, silvery-white ; one complete spikelet minus two outer glumes.

B. *Vegetative organs.*

Habit of growth—Tufted perennial.

Root system—Fibrous, yellowish-white.

Shoots—Rounded, glabrous, older shoots swollen at base.

Leaf sheath—Glabrous, split, brown in colour when old, slightly keeled.

Leaf blade—Light green, slightly keeled, blades rolled in shoot, sweet taste ; dries to silvery-grey colour, glabrous.

Auricles—Absent.

Ligule—White, membranous, prominent.

C. *Distribution.*

Indigenous to Europe and Asia. Abundant in Britain, and thrives best on low-lying, heavy soils.

D. *Economic value.*

Nutritive value and palatability high. Commercial types stemy. Indigenous leafy strains are available to suit different purposes. For grazing there are very prostrate, spreading types. For hay tall very leafy types. There are also intermediate types. Timothy is very susceptible to grazing, but produces very heavy hay crops on good soil. Sown in seeds mixtures for temporary and permanent leys, especially on heavy soil.

Fig. 26.—A. Inflorescence. B. Spikelet. C. Commercial seed. D. Vegetative organs. E. Outline of leaf blade. F. Junction of leaf sheath and blade. G. Section through leaf blade.

Annual Meadow Grass (Poa annua)

A. *Floral organs.*

Time of flowering—Almost throughout whole year.
Inflorescence—Panicle 1 to 3 inches long, loose, spreading culms 3 to 12 inches high.
Spikelets—Oblong to ovate, 3 to 6 flowered.
Glumes—Two, unequal.
Pales—Two, outer pale with minute silky hairs along keel.
Commercial seed—Single grain plus pales, plus rachilla.

B. *Vegetative organs.*

Habit of growth—Small, tufted annual.
Root system—Yellowish-brown, fibrous.
Shoots—Flat.
Leaf sheath—Split, glabrous.
Leaf blade—Light green, folded in shoot, blunt apex ; upper surface dull with two faint tram-like lines running longitudinally from apex to base ; glabrous.
Auricles—Absent.
Ligule—Long, membraneous.

C. *Distribution.*

Common in almost every part of the globe.   Most common in Britain as a weed in gardens, parks and waste places.

D. *Economic value.*

Nutritive value low, not recommended for sowing in seeds mixtures.

Fig. 27.—A. Inflorescence.   B. Spikelet.   C. Commercial seed.   D. Vegetative organs.   E. Outline of leaf blade.   F. Junction of leaf sheath and blade.   G. Section through leaf blade.

A

C ×10·6

B ×8

D

E

F

G

Smooth-stalked Meadow Grass (Poa pratensis)

A. *Floral organs.*

Time of flowering—May and June.

Inflorescence—Panicle erect, spreading at time of flowering ;
culms 1 to 2 feet high.

Spikelets—Ovate, 3 to 5 flowered.

Glumes—Two, unequal, keeled.

Pales—Two, upper one not pointed ; hairs along bottom
half of keel ; conspicuous web of hairs at base.

Commercial seed—Single grain plus pales, plus rachilla.

B. *Vegetative organs.*

Habit of growth—Creeping perennial (rhizomes).

Root system—Fibrous, tuft of roots at nodes of rhizomes.

Shoots—Flat.

Leaf sheath—Entire, glabrous, smooth.

Leaf blade—Dark green, folded in shoot, blunt apex, upper
surface dull ; two longitudinal lines from apex to base ;
keeled below, glabrous.

Auricles—Absent.

Ligule—Small throughout.

C. *Distribution.*

Indigenous to Europe, Asia and North America, and from
Mediterranean to Arctic circle. Common in Britain in rich, damp
meadows and pastures, also in dry hedgerows.

D. *Economic value.*

Nutritive value and palatability high. Sometimes recommended for sowing in seed mixtures as a bottom grass in open,
rich soils, and for hard-wearing lawns.

Fig. 28.—A. Inflorescence. B. Spikelet. C. Commercial seed. D. Vegetative organs. E. Outline of leaf blade. F. Junction of leaf sheath
and blade. G. Section through leaf blade.

Level of
Soil

×16.6

×10.6

Rough-stalked Meadow Grass (*Poa trivialis*)

A. *Floral organs.*

Time of flowering—July and August.

Inflorescence—Panicle erect, about 6 inches long with slender spreading branches ; culms 1 to 3 feet high.

Spikelets—Numerous, 2 to 5 flowers, usually two, seldom more than three, ovate, short stalks.

Glumes—Two, outer glume slightly longer than inner one ; keeled, minute hairs along keel.

Pales—Two, outer pale pointed ; web of hairs at base.

Commercial seed—Single grain plus pales, plus rachilla.

B. *Vegetative organs.*

Habit of growth—Loose spreading tufts.

Root system—Fibrous, small tufts at nodes on stolons.

Shoots—Flat, glabrous.

Leaf sheath—Not split, minute asperites on old sheath, glabrous.

Leaf blade—Dark green, shining below, keeled, apex pointed, hooded tip. Two tramline-like lines from apex to base ; glabrous.

Auricles—Absent.

Ligule—Short on lower leaves, long on upper ones.

C. *Distribution.*

Indigenous to Europe, Central Asia and America. Most common in Britain on rich, moist, heavy soils.

D. *Economic value.*

Nutritive value and palatability high. Productivity high during early summer. Persistent on account of its creeping habit. Sown in seeds mixtures for permanent leys as a bottom grass on rich, moist soil.

Fig. 29.—A. Inflorescence. B. Spikelet. C. Commercial seed. D. Vegetative organs. E. Outline of leaf blade. F. Junction of leaf sheath and blade. G. Section through leaf blade.

A

B ×10·6

C ×20

D   Level of Soil

E

F

G

Mountain Heath Grass (*Sieglingia decumbens*)

A. *Floral organs.*

Time of flowering—July.

Inflorescence—Panicle contracted into a simple raceme ; culms about 1 foot high.

Spikelets—Comparatively few in a panicle, 3 or 4 flowered.

Glumes—Two, equal, pointed, glabrous, keeled.

Pales—Two, outer one rounded on back, ending in three points ; a tuft of hairs at its base.

Commercial seed—Single grain plus pales, plus rachilla.

B. *Vegetative organs.*

Habit of growth—Tufted perennial.

Root system—Yellowish, fibrous, long.

Shoots—Flat.

Leaf sheath—Split, hairy.

Leaf blade—Folded in shoot, long, narrow, pointed, usually long, soft hairs along edges and underside ; ribless above, except for two parallel lines on each side of midrib.

Auricles—Absent.

Ligule—Represented by a tuft of hairs.

C. *Distribution.*

Indigenous to Europe. Common in Britain on dry heaths and hilly pastures.

D. *Economic value.*

Nutritive value low, used for rough grazing on heaths and hilly pastures.

Fig. 30.—A. Inflorescence. B. Spikelet. C. Commercial seed. D. Vegetative organs. E. Outline of leaf blade. F. Junction of leaf sheath and blade. G. Section through leaf blade.

A

D

C   ×8·6

E

B   ×6·6

F

G

Golden Oat Grass (*Trisetum flavescens*)

A. *Floral organs.*

Time of flowering—June and July.

Inflorescence—Panicle erect, slender, spreading branches, 3 to 5 inches long ; culms 1 to 2 feet high.

Spikelets—Numerous, small, erect, shining, yellowish, 2 to 3 flowers.

Glumes—Two, unequal, upper or inner glume approximatel three times as large as the lower one ; thin, pointed.

Pales—Two, outer pale with dorsal awn ; awn twisted, bent ; bifid apex ; inner pale thin, awnless ; tufts of hairs at base ; rachilla hairy.

Commercial seed—Single grain plus pales, plus rachilla.

B. *Vegetative organs.*

Habit of growth—Tufted perennial, erect.

Root system—Fibrous, yellow.

Shoots—Rounded.

Leaf sheath—Split, hairy.

Leaf blade—Light green ; hairs on both surfaces, hairs reflexed, ribbed above.

Auricles—Absent.

Ligule—Prominent.

C. *Distribution.*

Indigenous to Europe, Asia, Scandinavia and America. Most common in Britain on heavy soils containing a fair amount of lime.

D. *Economic value.*

Nutritive value and palatability high. Productivity low. High proportion of stem to leaf. Recommended for permanent seeds mixtures on suitable soils as a bottom grass.

Fig. 31.—A. Inflorescence. B. Spikelet. C. Commercial seed. D. Vegetative organs. E. Outline of leaf blade. F. Junction of leaf sheath and blade. G. Section through leaf blade.

A

B ×10

C ×12

D

E

F

G

CHAPTER 5

LEGUMINOSAE (CLOVER FAMILY)

As in the section on grasses the morphological features of Leguminous plants may be conveniently studied under two separate headings : (a) the Floral Organs, and (b) the Vegetative Organs.

The Floral Organs.

The flowers of clovers and other members of the Leguminosae family are usually brightly coloured, and arranged on a central axis to form a racemose type of inflorescence. The form of the inflorescence varies in different species ; in Red Clover the flowers are grouped together at the end of a main stem, whereas in Lucerne they arise in the axils of the leaves.

A single flower (Fig. 32 A) is often described as papilionaceous on account of its close resemblance to the common butterfly, and consists of 5 sepals (calyx), 5 petals (corolla), 10 stamens (androecium), and 1 carpel (gynaecium).

Calyx.—The five sepals are usually joined together to form a tube at the base, with the tip of each remaining free and appearing as five tooth-like projections (Fig. 32 B).

Corolla.—The petals are coloured and very irregular in shape, with a characteristic claw at the base of each. The upper or posterior petal is broad and conspicuous, and is commonly called the standard (Fig. 32 c). The two side or wing petals are usually free (Fig. 32 D), whilst the two lowermost ones are usually joined along their outer edges to form the keel (Fig. 32 E).

Androecium.—The filaments of the ten stamens (male organs) may be either all united to form a sheath surrounding the ovary (Fig. 32 F) or the upper one free and the other nine joined to form the sheath.

Gynaecium.—The single carpel (female organ) is usually surrounded by the stamens (Fig. 32 F). The ovary (Fig. 32 G) is one-celled, containing one or more ovules (Fig. 32 H), arranged

Fig. 32.—A. Flower of Gorse. B. Calyx. C. Standard petal. D. Wing petals. E. Keel petals. F. Stamens. G. Carpel. H. Longitudinal section through carpel. J. Fruit or pod. K. Mature pod split to release seed. L. Seed.
1. Bract ; 2. claws ; 3. sheath ; 4. filaments ; 5. anthers ; 6. style ; 7. stigma ; 8. ovules ; 9. seed.

along the upper edge of the cavity. The style varies in length
in the different species and is terminated by a sticky stigma.

Fertilisation.—The flowers of clovers are usually self-sterile,
and cross-pollination is carried out by insects and bees, which
seek the honey glands at the base of the stamens. When the
insects alight on the wing petals, the keel is automatically de-
pressed, causing the emergence of the stigma and stamens. The
visiting insect then becomes dusted with pollen, which is in turn
transferred to another flower of the same type.

The Fruit.—After fertilisation the ovary develops into a
fruit which, in the majority of cases, is termed a legume or pod
(Fig. 32 J). It varies in shape and size according to the species ;
in Lucerne (Fig. 39 F) it is spirally twisted and contains two or
three seeds, whereas in Red Clover it takes the form of an ovoid
one-seeded structure commonly called a pyxidium (Fig. 47 F).
The pod may split along both edges to release the seed with
great force as in Bird's-foot Trefoil, or along one side only as in
Wild White Clover and Gorse (Fig. 32 K).

The Seed.—The seeds are usually round to oval in shape with
a firm leathery seed-coat (Fig. 32 L). A scar or hilum is often
visible on the seed-coat where it was once joined to the ovary
wall (Fig. 33 G), and near this may be seen a minute hole called
the micropyle, which connects with the interior of the seed.
Within the seed coat are two seed-leaves or cotyledons, in between
which lie the radicle and plumule (Fig. 32 H). Upon germination
these develop into a root and shoot respectively (Fig. 33 J).

Germination.

With an adequate supply of water, air and temperature the
seeds begin to germinate. The cotyledons, which usually appear
above the ground, supply the young developing embryo with
reserved food material. The portion between the radicle and
the cotyledons (Fig. 33 D) is called the hypocotyl, and in clovers
this grows more rapidly than the epicotyl, which lies between
the plumule and the cotyledons (Fig. 33 E). In the Vetch the

FIG. 33.—A. Seed of Red Clover. B. Seed-coat removed. C. First stage in
    germination (epigeal). D. Second stage in germination. E. Third
    stage in germination. F. Fourth stage in germination. G. Seed of
    Vetch. H. Seed-coat and one cotyledon removed. J. First stage in
    germination (hypogeal). K. Second stage in germination.
1. Seed-coat ; 2. cotyledons ; 3. radicle ; 4. hypocotyl ; 5. plumule ;
    6. first leaf ; 7. second leaf ; 8. hilum ; 9. epicotyl.

epicotyl grows more rapidly than the hypocotyl and the cotyledons remain below the ground (Fig. 33 J).   In the clovers the plumule arises from a point between the cotyledons, and gradually develops into a stem, upon which are formed the first and subsequent leaves of the plant (Fig. 33 F). At the same time secondary rootlets arise on the radicle, and soon the plant is able to lead an independent existence, without the aid of the cotyledons.

The Leaves.

The leaves are arranged alternately on the stem (Fig. 36 B) and consist of a stalk or petiole, upon which may be borne two or more leaflets according to the family to which it belongs ; e.g. the clovers are trifoliate, with three leaflets (Fig. 34 B) and Sainfoin pinnate (Fig. 34 D), with several pairs of opposite leaflets. The terminal leaflet sometimes takes the form of a tendril as in Meadow Pea (Fig. 34 A). At the base of each leaf stalk may be found a pair of appendages common to all clovers called stipules (Fig. 34 B) and which may differ in shape, size and colour according to the species. These, together with other features, such as mucronate tips (Fig. 34 c), hairiness and colour, often serve as useful guides for identification purposes.

Root System.

The young radicle usually develops into a long tap root from which arise numerous secondary branches (Fig. 35 B).

Numerous small swellings called nodules appear, distributed in an irregular manner on the root system (Fig. 34 E, F). These are formed by a special type of bacteria (*Pseudomonas radicicola*) which find their way into the plant through the root hairs, and which are capable of fixing and absorbing into their system a certain amount of free nitrogen from the air in the soil. This nitrogen is made use of by the clover plant which in return supplies the bacteria with food material. As a result, the clover and all other leguminous plants are rich in protein, and this, together with the fact that the root systems enrich the soil in nitrogen, make the leguminous family one of the most important in agricultural practice.

Fig. 34.—A. Leaf of Meadow Pea.   B. Leaf of Red Clover.   C. Leaf of Lucerne.   D. Leaf of Sainfoin.   E. Nodules on roots of Sainfoin.   F. Nodules on roots of Red Clover.

1. Tendril ; 2. lateral leaflets ; 3. terminal leaflet ; 4. stipules ; 5. mucronate tip ; 6. petiole ; 7. lateral rootlets ; 8. nodules.

CHAPTER 6

KEY TO THE VEGETATIVE CHARACTERS OF SOME COMMON LEGUMES

I. Leaf simple.

A. Obcordate—First foliage leaf of *Clovers and Medicks*.

B. Oblong—Lowest leaves of *Kidney Vetch* (upper ones compound).

C. Spiny—Lowest leaves of *Gorse*.

II. Leaves bifoliate, terminating in a tendril   *Lathyrus pratensis*.

III. Leaves trifoliate.

A. Plants hairy.

  1. Mucronate tip .   .   .   .   .   *Medicago lupulina.*

  2. Tip not mucronate.

    (*a*) Straggling habit, terminal leaflet at a distance from the rest .   .   .   .   .   .   *Trifolium dubium.*

    (*b*) Prostrate habit, pubescence silky, leaves obcordate, annual .   .   .   .   *Trifolium subterraneum.*

    (*c*) Upright habit.

      (i) Stipules blunt, with purple border at apex

                  Trifolium incarnatum.

      (ii) Stipules pointed.

        α. Stipules adherent to petiole, frequently with red lines .   .   .   .   .   *Trifolium pratense.*

        β. Stipules free from petiole, narrow and pointed ; stems zig-zagging .   .   .   *Trifolium medium.*

B. Plants hairless.

  1. Tip not mucronate.

    (*a*) Upright habit .   .   .   .   *Trifolium hybridum.*

    (*b*) Straggling habit.

      (i) Rooting at nodes .   .   .   *Trifolium repens.*

      (ii) Not rooting at nodes .   .   .   *Trifolium dubium.*

2. Tip mucronate ;   edge coarsely serrated round apex only
Medicago sativa.

IV. Leaves pentafoliate.

Three terminal leaflets and one pair of stipule-like leaflets at base
Lotus corniculatus.

V. Leaflets more than five.

A. Terminal leaflet present.

1. Terminal leaflet no longer than others.

   (*a*) Softly nairy with lowest pair close to the stem
Ornithopus perpusillus.

   (*b*) Glabrous above, slightly downy underneath ;   stipules
pointed, brown or pink   .   .   . *Onobrychis sativa.*

2. Terminal leaflet longer than others   *Anthyllis vulneraria.*

B. Terminal leaflet replaced by tendril.

1. Tip mucronate, dark spot on stipule, stipule toothed
Vicia sativa.

2. Tip not mucronate.

   (*a*) Four to six pairs leaflets   .   .   . *Vicia sepium.*

   (*b*) About ten pairs leaflets .   .   .   . *Vicia cracca.*

CHAPTER 7

BOTANICAL DESCRIPTIONS OF LEGUMINOSAE FAMILY

Kidney Vetch (*Anthyllis vulneraria*)

A. *Floral organs.*

Time of flowering—July.

Inflorescence—Flower heads usually in pairs at the ends of the stems, each one subtended by a divided bract.

Flowers—Numerous on short stalks ; calyx 5, inflated, hairy, narrow at the mouth ; petals 5, yellow to red, small ; stamens all united ; ovary with 2 ovules ; stalked.

Fruit—Flat pod, black, one-seeded.

Seed—Oval, 2·5 mm. long, green at base and yellow near apex ; smooth.

B. *Vegetative organs.*

Seedling—Cotyledons above ground ; first leaf simple, long, slightly hairy.

Habit of growth—Tufted perennial.

Stems—Erect, and mostly produced in second year, 12 to 18 inches long, slightly hairy.

Leaves—During first year mostly simple, forming rosette, later pinnate with large terminal leaflets ; which spring from axil of simple leaves, slightly hairy ; stipules small, ledge-like.

Root system—Tap root long, numerous secondary roots ; nodules large.

C. *Distribution.*

Indigenous to Europe and Western Asia, and from Mediterranean to Arctic regions. Most common in Britain in dry pastures on calcareous soils.

D. *Economic value.*

Sown in drills, or broadcast alone, on dry poor calcareous soils (20 lb. per acre) for sheep grazing. It may be sown also in seeds mixtures for permanent leys on such soils.

FIG. 35.—A. Seedling. B. Complete plant. C. Leaf. D. Inflorescence. E. Floret. F. Fruit. G. Seed.

Meadow Pea (*Lathyrus pratensis*)

A. *Floral organs.*

Time of flowering—June and July.

Inflorescence—Short raceme of 6 to 10 flowers, on end of long stalks.

Flowers—Prominent, calyx 5, sharply pointed, hairy; petals 5, yellow, standard broad; stamens 10, upper one free; ovary containing several ovules; style flat.

Fruit—Pod almost glabrous, seeds several.

Seed—Globular, dark brown.

B. *Vegetative organs.*

Seedling—Cotyledons remain below ground; first leaf with one pair leaflets, and one pair sharply pointed stipules, no tendrils.

Habit of growth—Straggling to half-climbing perennial.

Stems—1 to 2 feet long, weak, straggly.

Leaves—One pair leaflets, short stalk; leaflets linear; tendrils; stipules pointed, prominent teeth at base.

Root system—Slender tap root, numerous branches.

C. *Distribution.*

Indigenous to Europe and Asia. Abundant in Britain in moist meadows and hedgerows.

D. *Economic value.*

On account of a low production of leaf, the plant is not cultivated, but it is sometimes eaten by cattle in the wild state.

Fig. 36.—A. Seedling. B. Complete plant. C. Leaf. D. Inflorescence. E. Floret. F. Fruit. G. Seed.

Bird's-foot Trefoil (*Lotus corniculatus*)

A. *Floral organs.*

Time of flowering—June and July.

Inflorescence—Umbel-like cymes at the end of long axillary branches.

Flowers—4 to 6 in number ; calyx 5, teeth not spreading ; petals 5, yellow, standard often tinged red ; keel petals joined, tubular at apex, through which the stigma and pollen emerge when pollinated by bees ; self-sterile ; ovary contains numerous ovules.

Fruit—Pod about 1 to 2 inches long, containing numerous seeds which are released by sudden splitting of the pod along both edges.

Seed—Small rounded, kidney shaped, 1·5 to 2 mm. long ; shiny, dark brown or chocolate.

B. *Vegetative organs.*

Seedling—Cotyledons above ground, short stalks ; long epicotyl ; first and second leaves trifoliate.

Habit of growth—Spreading to erect perennial.

Stems—Numerous, about 12 inches long, sometimes hairy.

Leaves—Trifoliate, alternate, short stalks ; a pair of leaf-like stipules at base of petiole ; sometimes hairy.

Root system—Tap root, long, numerous secondary rootlets and nodules.

C. *Distribution.*

Indigenous to Europe, Asia and Australia. Most common in Britain on light soils.

D. *Economic value.*

Usually sown in seeds mixtures on land which is too light and poor to support other clovers. Lotus major, distinguished by its spreading calyx, prefers damp shady places, and is profitably sown on such soils.

Fig. 37.—A. Seedling. B. Complete plant. C. Leaf. D. Inflorescence. F. Fruit. G. Seed.

A

B

C

D

G

×16.6

F

× ·6

Trefoil, Black Medick, Hop Clover (*Medicago lupulina*)

A. *Floral organs.*

Time of flowering—July.

Inflorescence—Compact raceme, oval in shape, borne at the ends of long axillary branches.

Florets—Bright yellow, small, numerous; calyx 5, equal; petals 5, standard petal large; ovary containing one ovule; after fertilisation the ovary becomes twisted and black.

Fruit—Pod, one-seeded, small, slightly hairy, curved almost into complete ring.

Seed—Plump, greenish-yellow, shining, 2 mm. long; definite projection where radicle ends.

B. *Vegetative organs.*

Seedling—Cotyledons above ground, almost round, short stalks; first leaf simple with a distinct projecting mid-rib (mucronate tip), slightly hairy.

Habit of growth—Annual, stem spreading, sub-erect.

Stems—1 to 2 feet long, hairy.

Leaves—Trifoliate, leaflets sometimes hairy with long stalk to terminal one; ovate in shape with projecting mid-rib (mucronate tip); stipules serrated and very pointed.

Root system—Tap root, long; numerous nodules.

C. *Distribution.*

Indigenous to Europe and Asia. Most common in Britain on calcareous soils.

D. *Economic value.*

Not recommended in seeds mixtures except in small quantities for temporary leys on dry, chalky soil. It is sometimes sown on such soils with corn crops, to plough in later with the stubble as a green manure.

Fig. 38.—A. Seedling. B. Complete plant. C. Leaf. D. Inflorescence. E. Floret. F. Fruit. G. Seed.

7

Alfalfa, Lucerne (*Medicago sativa*)

A. *Floral organs.*

Time of flowering—July and August.

Inflorescence—Close raceme, borne on axillary stalks, spreading from the axils of leaves on main stem.

Flowers—Violet to blue, sometimes yellow ; short stalks subtended by small bracts at base ; calyx 5 teeth, petals 5 ; stamens 10, upper one free ; ovary with numerous ovules ; cross-fertilised by bees.

Fruit—Dehiscent pod, spirally twisted, several seeds.

Seed—Irregular, kidney shape to oval ; point of radicle not prominent ; usually bent appearance, 2 to 3 mm. long, yellowish-brown.

B. *Vegetative organs.*

Seedling—Cotyledons above ground, with short stalks ; first leaf simple, glabrous (mucronate tip) ; internode of epicotyl elongated bearing second leaf, presenting a long seedling, not rosette as in most other clovers.

Habit of growth—Erect perennial, tufted after first year.

Stems—1 to 2 feet long, glabrous, numerous in second year, arising from lower nodes of older stems and from axils of cotyledons.

Leaves—Trifoliate, short stalks ; leaflets may be hairy, upper margin serrated ; mucronate tip; stipules broad, serrated, sharply pointed.

Root system—Usually tap root, sometimes tap roots are branched giving out aerial roots ; numerous nodules when soil inoculated.

C. *Distribution.*

Indigenous to Europe, Asia and America. Most common in Britain on deep calcareous soils in south and east.

D. *Economic value.*

Recommended for sowing alone in drills on suitable soils ; seeding, 30 to 40 lb. per acre. Usually cut green or fed off. Known to produce five cuts in one season. Used in manufacture of Lucerne meal.

Fig. 39.—A. Seedling. B. Complete plant. C. Leaf. D. Inflorescence E. Floret. F_1. Collection of fruits. F_2. Single fruit. G. Seed.

Common Bird's-foot (*Ornithopus perpusillus*)

A. *Floral organs.*

Time of flowering—June and July.

Inflorescence—2 to 4 flower heads at the end of long axillary branches.

Flowers—Almost sessile, subtended by a small leaf ; calyx 5, prominent teeth, hairy ; petals pinkish-white ; stamens 10, upper one free ; ovary slightly flattened, long, several ovules.

Fruit—Pods, slightly hairy, ending in a curved beak, separating when ripe into short, oval, one-seeded parts.

Seed—Yellow, oval with flattened ends.

B. *Vegetative organs.*

Seedling—Cotyledons above ground, long stalks ; first leaf compound, 4 to 5 pairs leaflets.

Habit of growth—Prostrate to sub-erect, annual.

Stems—6 to 12 inches long, round, slightly hairy.

Leaves—Compound ; leaflets 5 to 20 pairs, opposite, hairy ; lowest pair close to the stem ; stipules small.

Root system—Tap root, numerous fine, secondary branches.

C. *Distribution.*

Indigenous to Southern and Central Europe and Sweden. Most common in Britain in sandy and gravelly places.

D. *Economic value.*

Useful for green manuring on light, sandy soil.

Fig. 40.—A. Seedling. B. Complete plant. C. Leaf. D. Inflorescence. E. Floret. F$_1$. Collection of fruits. F$_2$. Portion of fruit. G. Seed.

D

C

F₁

×2·6

E

B

F₂

×10·6

G

×13·3

A

Sainfoin (*Onobrychis sativa*)

A. *Floral organs.*

Time of flowering—June and July.

Inflorescence—Compact raceme, borne on long axillary branches ; later, flowers separate due to elongation of stalk.

Florets—Pale pink with dark red veins about 1 inch long ; calyx 5, long teeth ; petals 5—wing petals shorter than keel and standard ; stamens 10, upper one free ; ovary round, one ovule.
with veins ; lower edge bordered with short teeth ; one-seeded.

Seed (milled)—Kidney shaped, prominent radicle, 4 to 5 mm. long, greenish-brown, bright.

B. *Vegetative organs.*

Seedling—Cotyledons above ground, thick, fleshy, sessile ; first leaf simple, oval, second leaf trifoliate, fourth leaf pinnate.

Habit of growth—Erect perennial.

Stems—1 to 2 feet high, round, slightly hairy.

Leaves—Pinnate, 6 to 12 pairs leaflets, plus a terminal one, slightly hairy below ; projecting mid-rib ; stipules thin, finely-pointed, browning with age.

Root system—Tap root, long, thick and fleshy, numerous nodules.

C. *Distribution.*

Indigenous to Southern Europe and temperate Asia. Most common in Britain in south on calcareous soils.

D. *Economic value.*

Two varieties—(1) Common Sainfoin, (2) Giant Sainfoin. Common Sainfoin persists for a number of years, cut for hay in the first year, afterwards foraged or grazed. Giant Sainfoin lasts for two years only, cut for hay, or foraged and grazed. Both varieties are drilled with Barley on light calcareous soils in the south. Rate of seeding 50 lb. milled and 100 lb. unmilled per acre.

Fig. 41.—A. Seedling. B. Complete plant. C. Leaf. D. Inflorescence. E. Floret. F_1. Collection of fruits. F_2. Single fruit (unmilled seed). G. Seed.

F₁

C

D

E

F₂
×3·3

A

B

G
×3·3

Lesser Burnet (*Poterium Sanguisorba* (*Rosaceae*))

A. *Floral organs.*

Time of flowering—July.

Inflorescence—Flower heads arranged in dense ovate heads, at the end of long axillary stalks.

Flowers—Numerous, light green in colour, often with a reddish tinge ; lower flowers all males, upper ones female ; numerous hanging stamens ; long style, tufted stigma ; calyx 4 lobed ; petals absent ; ovary containing 1 or 2 ovules.

Fruit—Brown, quadrangular nut, irregularly pitted surfaces, usually one seed ; fruit often an impurity in unmilled Sainfoin seed.

Seed—Yellowish-brown, oval, pointed, flattened surface on one side, 2 mm. long.

B. *Vegetative organs.*

Seedling—Cotyledons above ground, long stalks, notched near petiole ; first leaf trifoliate, serrated edge.

Habit of growth—Erect perennial.

Stems—12 to 18 inches long, slightly hairy, angular.

Leaves—Compound, leaflets small, oval, serrated edges, slightly hairy.

Root system—Tap root, numerous stout branches.

C. *Distribution.*

In dry places and limestone clefts in Southern Europe, Asia and Sweden. Most common in Britain in limestone districts.

D. *Economic value.*

Nutritive value less than Sainfoin, which should replace it in seeds mixtures for light calcareous soils. Sainfoin and Burnet often grow together, and Burnet seed often occurs as an impurity in a Sainfoin sample. Burnet belongs to the Rosaceae family and does not possess nodules on its root system.

Fig. 42.—A. Seedling. B. Complete plant. C. Leaf. D. Inflorescence. F. Fruit. G. Seed.

B

D

A

C

G ×9·3

F ×6·6

Yellow Suckling Clover (*Trifolium dubium*)

A. *Floral organs.*

Time of flowering—July.

Inflorescence—Small terminal raceme ; round to oval in shape.

Florets—Yellow, numbering about 12 in each head ; calyx 5, short teeth ; petals 5, standard narrow ; stamens 10 ; ovary one ovule ; usually self-sterile.

Fruit—One-seeded pod.

Seed—Oval, radicle scarcely visible ; about 1·5 mm. long ; colour yellow to dark olive ; shiny.

B. *Vegetative organs.*

Seedling—Cotyledons above ground, oval, distinctly stalked ; first leaf glabrous, broader than long.

Habit of growth—Sub-erect to prostrate annual, sometimes persists two years.

Stems—Long, 18 to 24 inches, wiry, turning red.

Leaves—Trifoliate, short stalks ; leaflets small, sometimes slightly hairy, the central leaflet with longer stalk than the other two ; stipules broad at base, sharply pointed.

Root system—Short tap root, numerous nodules.

C. *Distribution.*

Indigenous to most of Europe. Most common in Britain in the south and east on poor soils.

D. *Economic value.*

On account of its low leaf production it is not recommended for sowing in seeds mixtures, except in small quantities, 2 to 4 lb. per acre, on light poor soils.

Fig. 43.—A. Seedling. B. Complete plant. C. Leaf. D. Inflo escence. E. Floret. F. Fruit. G. Seed.

A

B

C

D

E

F ×10·6

G ×13·3

Alsike Clover (*Trifolium hybridum*)

A. *Floral organs.*

Time of flowering—June and July.

Inflorescence—Raceme globular, arising on long stalks springing from the axils of leaves on the main stem.

Florets—Pale pink or white ; calyx 5, equal length ; petals 5, free ; ovary containing 1 to 3 ovules ; self-sterile, fertilised by bees.

Fruit—Pod, 1 to 3 seeds, indehiscent.

Seed—Heart-shaped, due to the radicle projecting to more than half length of seed ; approximately 1 mm. long ; greenish-brown in colour, becoming darker with age ; bright, smooth.

B. *Vegetative organs.*

Seedling—Cotyledons above ground, oval ; first leaf simple, almost oval, glabrous.

Habit of growth—Upright habit, persists 3 to 6 years.

Stems—Glabrous, branched, 2 to 3 feet high.

Leaves—Trifoliate ; leaflets obovate, glabrous ; lower edges of leaflets slightly serrated ; stipules tapering to a point, greenish veins.

Root system—Tap root, numerous secondary rootlets ; nodules numerous.

C. *Distribution.*

Indigenous to Europe ; abundant in Sweden. Not indigenous to Britain.

D. *Economic value.*

Sown in seeds mixtures in Britain on heavy damp soils, and will usually thrive where Red Clover fails, on account of soil acidity and clover sickness.

Fig. 44.—A. Seedling. B. Complete plant. C. Leaf. D. Inflorescence. E. Floret. F. Fruit. G. Seed.

Crimson Clover (*Trifolium incarnatum*)

A. *Floral organs.*

Time of flowering—July.

Inflorescence—Terminal raceme, some distance above last leaf on stem, oblong to cylindrical, sometimes 2 inches long.

Florets—Rich crimson, calyx 5, long, hairy; petals 5; stamens 10; ovary one ovule; usually self-sterile, fertilised by bees.

Fruit—One-seeded pod.

Seed—Oval, radicle small and scarcely seen on outside; 2·5 mm. long, shiny, yellowish-brown.

B. *Vegetative organs.*

Seedling—Cotyledons above ground; first leaf large, broad, hairy, lobed at base.

Habit of growth—Erect annual.

Stems—1 to 2 feet high, extremely hairy, few side branches.

Leaves—Trifoliate, long stalks near base of stem; leaflets obovate to obcordate, hairy; stipules broad, blunt apex, the older stipules often possessing a purple margin.

Root system—Long, finely branched; numerous nodules.

C. *Distribution.*

Indigenous in open places in Southern Europe. Not found wild in Britain, except for a wild white variety in Cornwall.

D. *Economic value.*

Used as a catch crop or a green manuring crop in South of England. Sown after cereals in autumn, and fed off or cut for hay in June; seed rate per acre about 20 lb.

Fig. 45.—A. Seedling. B. Complete plant. C. Leaf. D. Inflorescence. E. Floret. F. Fruit. G. Seed.

A

B

C

D

E

F   ×13·3

G   ×9·3

Wild Red Clover (*Trifolium pratense, spontaneum*)

A. *Floral organs.*

Time of flowering—April and May.

Inflorescence—Terminal raceme on main stem, oval to globular, 1 to 1½ inches long; subtended by two almost sessile trifoliate leaves.

Florets—Approximately 30 in number, self-sterile, pollinated by bees, pink to various shades of red, calyx hairy, 5 teeth, inferior one longer than others; petals 5, narrow, jointed at base, and attached to staminal tube of 9 stamens, the upper stamen free; ovary small, 2 ovules.

Fruit—One-seeded pyxidium, splitting transversely in half to release seed.

Seed—Oval, 1·5 mm. to 2 mm. long; shiny, upper half yellowish, lower half purple; small projection near base covering radicle.

B. *Vegetative organs.*

Seedling—Cotyledons above ground, oval; first leaf simple, round, hairy.

Habit of growth—Sub-erect to prostrate, straggly perennial.

Stems—Solid, wiry, may or may not possess hairs.

Leaves—Trifoliate; leaflets ovate, dark green, sometimes hairy, with light markings on upper surface. Stipules membraneous, frequently with purple veins; finely pointed.

Root system—Stout tap root; numerous nodules.

C. *Distribution.*

Indigenous to Europe and Asia, and from Mediterranean to Arctic regions. Most common in Britain in fertile meadows.

D. *Economic value.*

On account of the low proportion of leaf to stem it is not recommended for seeds mixtures.

Fig. 46.—A. Seedling. B. Complete plant. C. Leaf. D. Inflorescence. E. Floret. F. Fruit. G. Seed.

A. *Broad Red Clover* (*Trifolium pratense, præcox*)

Broad Red or Early-flowering Red Clover is a cultivated variety and differs from Wild Red in the following respects : (*a*) Time of flowering about 14 to 21 days later ; (*b*) leaves larger and distinctly broader ; (*c*) stems hollow, more erect, less numerous ; (*d*) persists for two years only ; (*e*) frequently sown in seeds mixtures on good soils for temporary leys of one or two years' duration ; (*f*) provides early spring growth and an excellent aftermath in the first year.

During recent years numerous strains have been compared at the Welsh Plant Breeding Station, Aberystwyth. Results have shown that the British strains, viz. Dorset Marl, Vale of Clwyd, Vale of Glamorgan and Cotswold, are superior to the foreign types.

B. *Late-flowering Red Clover or Single Cut Cow Grass* (*Trifolium pratense, serotinum*)

This variety is more persistent (4 to 5 years) and as a result is more widely cultivated than Broad Red. It often possesses more stems per plant and produces flowers about 14 days later. The first year's hay crop is usually heavy, but spring and aftermath growth is definitely below that of Broad Red. During the second and succeeding years it surpasses Broad Red in every respect. On account of its persistency and high productivity it is always recommended for seeding down permanent leys on good soils. Strains, such as Cornish Marl, Montgomery Red, Cotswold and Essex, have yielded better results than the foreign strains.

Fig. 47.—A. Seedling. B. Complete plant. C. Leaf. D. Inflorescence. E. Floret. F. Fruit. G. Seed.

×13·3

F

B

C

×13·3

G

A

E

D

White Clover (*Trifolium repens*)

A. *Floral organs.*

Time of flowering—May to August.

Inflorescence—Almost spherical, produced at the end of long stalks, which spring from the axils of the leaves on the stolons.

Florets—White, sometimes tinged pink ; calyx 5, equal ; petals 5, joined to stamens at base, becoming brown and deflexed later ; ovary 4 to 6 ovules.

Fruit—Pod, 2 to 3 seeds, splitting along one side to release seeds.

Seed—Heart-shaped, radicle projecting to half the length of seed ; approximately 1 mm. long, bright yellow to yellowish-brown,.

B. *Vegetative organs.*

Seedling—Cotyledons above ground, first leaf round, glabrous, slightly serrated edges.

Habit of growth—Prostrate creeping perennial, stoloniferous.

Stems—Solid, possessing adventitious roots at the nodes ; glabrous.

Leaves—Trifoliate, leaflets obovate, serrated edges, with or without markings on upper surface, glabrous ; stipules small, pointed.

Root system—Stout tap root on main plant, with adventitious roots on nodes of stems.

C. *Distribution.*

Indigenous to Europe and Asia. Common in Britain on all rich pastures.

D. *Economic value.*

Wild White clover is often sown in seeds mixtures, on account of its high nutritive value and persistency. S.100 White clover is distinguished from Wild White by its larger leaves, earlier growth, and greater productivity, and from ordinary or Dutch White clover by its denser growth and greater persistency.

FIG. 48.—A. Seedling. B. Complete plant. C. Leaf. D. Inflorescence. E. Floret. F. Fruit. G. Seed.

Subterranean Clover (*Trifolium subterraneum*)

A. *Floral organs.*

Time of flowering—June and July.

Inflorescence—2 to 5 flowers together, at the end of long axillary branches, which lengthen after flowering and turn downwards.

Florets—White or pale pink ; calyx 5, teeth long ; petals 5, standard long ; after fertilisation the flowers become reversed and rest on the surface of the soil, and at the same time several short thick fibres, each with 5 teeth, rapidly develop around the base of the flower, which firmly fix the fruit in the soil.

Fruit—Pod, one-seeded, 2 to 3 pods may be present, enclosed in the thick fibres forming a burr.

Seed—Oval, dark purplish in colour.

B. *Vegetative organs.*

Seedling—Cotyledons above ground, long erect stalks ; first leaf hairy.

Habit of growth—Prostrate annual.

Stems—Prostrate, stout, hairy, sometimes reaching from 4 to 6 feet in length.

Leaves—Trifoliate, long stalks ; leaflets hairy, obovate, often prominent purplish veins ; stipules broad, finely pointed.

Root system—Tap root, numerous nodules, no adventitious roots at nodes.

C. *Distribution.*

Indigenous to dry sandy soils in Southern Europe. Common in South and Central England.

D. *Economic value.*

Used in Australia as a fodder plant. Would probably be a useful ingredient in British seeds mixtures, if sufficient care were taken to permit re-seeding by removing stock at time of flowering.

FIG. 49.—A. Seedling. B. Complete plant. C. Leaf. D. Changes in position of floral organs. E. Burr. F. Fruit. G. Seed.

Common Vetch (*Vicia sativa*)

A. *Floral organs.*

Time of flowering—Spring and early summer.

Inflorescence—Flowers borne singly, or in pairs on short stalks in the axil of leaves on the main stem.

Flowers—Large, calyx 5 teeth, hairy; petals 5, reddish-purple; stamens 10, upper one free; ovary sometimes hairy, 4 to 10 ovules.

Fruit—Pod, 1 to 2 inches long, 4 to 10 seeds.

Seed—Dark brown, 5 mm. long, round.

B. *Vegetative organs.*

Seedling—Cotyledons remain below ground; first leaf with one pair leaflets, no tendrils.

Habit of growth—Trailing annual.

Stems—Numerous, long, nearly erect, almost climbing, weak, square, and slightly hairy.

Leaves—Pinnate, alternate on stems; 6 to 7 pairs opposite leaflets, mucronate tip, tendrils branched; stipules toothed, pointed, with sometimes a dark purple blotch in centre.

Root system—Tap root, slender, branching freely; nodules large.

C. *Distribution.*

Indigenous to Europe and certain parts of Asia. Most common in Britain on dry soils.

D. *Economic value.*

Two cultivated varieties, winter and spring sown. Both varieties are used for green fodder, either sown alone or with Oats, Barley, Rye or Beans (2 bushels of Oats to 1½ bushels of Vetches). Vetches make a very useful green feed for sheep and other live stock.

Fig. 50.   A. Seedling.   B. Complete plant.   C. Leaf.   E. Flower.   F. Fruit.
   G. Seed.

Ground
Level

A

B

C

E

F   ×1·3

G   ×3·3

REFERENCES

The Chemical Composition of Eleven Species and Strains of Grasses at Different Stages of Maturity." *Welsh J. Agric.*, 1931. T. W. Fagan & W. E. J. Milton.

The Rye Grass Seed Industry of Northern Ireland. S. P. Mercer.

" Studies in the Formation of Permanent Pastures in North Wales." *Welsh J. Agric.*, 1926. R. A. Roberts.

" The Hybridisation of Grasses," Welsh Plant Breeding Station, Aberystwyth. *Bull. Ser. H*, No. 2.

" Red Clover Investigations," Welsh Plant Breeding Station. *Bull. Ser. H*, No. 7, 1919–26.

Young Farmers' Club Booklets, Nos. 6, 12, 14, 16. Oaklings, Canons Close, Radlett, Herts.

The Farming Year, J. A. Scott Watson. Longmans, Green & Co., 1938.

The New Farming, D. H. Robinson. Nelson, 1938.

Collins-Longman's Study Atlas. Longmans, Green & Co., and Collins.

Grassland Management for the Practical Farmer, W. R. Peel. Macmillan, 1938.

Weeds of Grassland, H. C. Long. Ministry of Agriculture Bulletin No. 41. His Majesty's Stationery Office.

The Land of Britain. The Land Utilization Survey. Report in 92 County parts.

Improvement of Grassland, Ministry of Agriculture Bulletin No. 3. His Majesty's Stationery Office.

The Ploughing-up Policy and Ley-Farming, Sir George Stapledon. Faber & Faber.

British Grasses, S. F. Armstrong. Cambridge University Press, 1937.

Agricultural Botany, John Percival. Duckworth, 1936.

Leguminous Forage Plants, D. H. Robinson. Arnold, 1937.

Grassland, R. G. Stapledon and J. A. Hanley. Oxford University Press, 1927.

Methods of Pasture Analysis. Reprinted from *Agricultural Progress*, 1933, and obtainable from the Secretary, Agricultural Education Association, The University of Reading.

Report on Experiments at Dauntsey's School. Copies are obtainable from the Headmaster, Dauntsey's School, West Lavington, Wilts.

GLOSSARY

Aggressive species.—One that grows rapidly and tends to smother out other species in the sward, e.g. Italian Rye-grass.

Asperites.—Little projections on the leaves, making them harsh and unpalatable.

Awn.—An extension of the pale into a bristle-like appendage.

Bacteria.—Unicellular, non-green organism, usually classified in the Plant Kingdom.

Bifoliate.—A leaf possessing two leaflets.

Bract.—A modified leaf.

Carpel.—A one-celled seed vessel, or one of the component members of a compound pistil or seed vessel.

Caryopsis.—A fruit in which the seed-coat is fused to the ovary wall.

Cleistogamous.—Flowers which never expand and are systematically self-fertilised.

Coleoptile.—The first leaf to appear when grasses germinate.

Coleorhiza.—The sheath which encloses the young rootlets of grasses when they germinate.

Commercial seed.—The seeds of grasses are usually sold in the form of fruits. (See Caryopsis.)

Cotyledons.—A seed leaf or first leaf of the embryo. According to the number of cotyledons, plants may be monocotyledonous or dicotyledonous.

Cross fertilise.—The male gametes of one plant fertilising the female gamete of another plant.

Downy.—Short soft hairs.

Embryo.—The rudimentary form of any living thing in its first stage of development.

Endosperm.—Food reserve material in seeds.

Enzyme.—A chemical compound of vegetable or animal origin, which is capable of creating a chemical change, and in itself remaining unchanged in the process.

Epicotyl.—The portion of a young stem of an embryo above the cotyledons.

Filament.—Stalk.

Germination.—The first act of growth in a seed.

Glabrous.—Without hairs.

Glaucous.—With a bluish-green colour and a shiny bloom.

Glume.—A chaff-like scale or bract enclosing the flowers of grasses.

Gramineae.—The botanical Natural Order of grasses.

Hirsute.—When hairs are dense and not stiff.

Hypocotyl.—The part of the stem of an embryo below the cotyledons.

Hypogynous.—When the stalks of the stamens arise below the ovary on the axis of a flower.

Indigenous.—Plants which are native to, and grow wild in a country.

Inflorescence.—Flowers borne collectively on an axis.

Internode.—The part between two nodes or joints of a stem.

Leguminosae.—The botanical Natural Order to which clovers, medicks, vetches, etc., belong.

Ley.—Sown down to grass in a rotation of crops.

Lodicule.—A delicate scale found between the stamens and pales in grasses.

Membraneous.—A thin sheet-like structure, usually translucent.

Morphology.—A study of the form and structure of plants and animals.

Motor cells.—Thin walled cells near the mid-rib of grasses, semi-transparent and capable of losing and gaining water, which control the expansion of the leaves, and loss of moisture from the plant.

Mucronate.—Ending abruptly in a short, sharp point.

Nitrogen.—A tasteless, odourless, colourless inactive gas.

Node.—Joint of a stem.

Obcordate.—Heart-shaped leaf, with the notch opposite the stem.

Obovate.—Inversely ovate, leaf with point of attachment at the narrow end.

Ovary.—The female organ of plants and animals in which are produced the unfertilised seed or eggs.

Pale.—The inner bract of a grass flower.

Plumule.—The first bud of an embryo, or the first bud above the cotyledons.

Pollen.—Dust-like grains formed within the anthers of flowers ; the male element of flowering plants.

Pubescent.—See " Downy."

Radicle.—Root-like part of an embyro.

Rhizome.—A creeping subterranean stem, usually producing roots and leaves at its nodes.

"S" Strains.—Strains bred from wild or indegenous species.

Scutellum.—The supposed cotyledon of grass seeds, lying between the embryo and endosperm.

Self-fertile.—A flower which fertilises itself.

Self-sterile.—A flower which is incapable of fertilising itself.

Stamen.—The pollen-bearing organ of a flower.

Stigma.—The part of a pistil which receives the pollen.

Stipule.—One of the pair of appendages found at the base of a petiole of certain leaves, e.g. *Leguminosae* family.

Stolon.—A creeping stem above ground, which usually roots at the nodes.

Sward.—A turf, or the surface of soil thickly covered with grass and clover.

Tendril.—A slender leafless organ produced by the modification of a stem or leaf, and which enables the plant to climb and coil itself round a support.

Tiller.—A shoot from the base of a stem.

INDEX

		PAGE
Agropyrum repens. Couch grass	. . . . .	14, 15, 18
Agrostis tenuis. Bent grass	. . . .	16, 20
Alopecurus agrestis. Slender foxtail	. . . .	16
,, *geniculatus.* Floating foxtail	. . .	16
,, *pratensis.* Meadow foxtail	. . .	10, 16, 22
Ammophila arenaria. Marram grass	. . .	13, 24
Anthoxanthum odoratum. Sweet vernal	. .	1, 2, 15, 26
Anthyllis vulneraria. Kidney vetch	. . .	80, 81, 82
Arrhenatherum avenaceum. Tall oat grass	. .	2, 9, 17, 28
Avena pratensis. Perennial oat grass	. . .	14, 30
,, *pubescens.* Downy oat grass	. . .	13
Barley	. . . .	4
Brachypodium pinnatum. Heath false brome	. .	32
,, *sylvaticum.* Wood false brome	. .	15, 34
Briza media. Quaking grass	. . . .	14
Bromus asper. Wood brome grass	. . . .	14
,, *mollis.* Soft brome grass	. . .	15, 36
,, *sterilis.* Barren brome grass	. . .	15
Chemical composition of grasses	. . . .	10
Cynosurus cristatus. Crested dogstail	. . .	13, 16, 38
Dactylis glomerata. Cocksfoot	. .	9, 11, 13, 40
Deschampsia caespitosa. Tufted hair grass	. .	13, 42
,, *flexuosa.* Wavy hair grass	. .	12, 44
Digraphis arundinacea. Reed canary grass	. . .	16
Elymus arenarius. Sand lyme grass	. . .	14
Festuca elatior. Tall fescue	. . . .	10
,, *ovina.* Sheep's fescue	. . . .	12, 46
,, *pratensis.* Meadow fescue	. . .	14, 48
,, *rubra.* Red fescue	. . . .	10, 50
Glyceria aquatica. Manna grass	. . . .	12
,, *fluitans.* Floating sweet grass	. . .	12

Grasses, general—   PAGE
   Description of auricle 8
         „   „ commercial seed 2
         „   „ flower 2
         „   „ germination 4
         „   „ inflorescence 1
         „   „ leaf blade 6
         „   „ leaf sheath 6
         „   „ leaves 6
         „   „ ligule 8
         „   „ root system 8
         „   „ spikelet 1
         „   „ true seed 4
         „   „ young shoot 6

Holcus lanatus. Yorkshire fog 2, 10, 15, 52
  „ *mollis*. Creeping soft grass 15
Hordeum murinum. Wall barley grass 15
  „ *pratense*. Meadow barley grass 14

Koeleria cristata. Crested hair grass 16

Lathyrus pratensis. Meadow pea 80, 84
Legumes—
   General description of carpels 74
      „   „   „ fertilisation 76
      „   „   „ floral organs 74
      „   „   „ fruit 76
      „   „   „ germination 76
      „   „   „ leaves 78
      „   „   „ petals 74
      „   „   „ root system 78
      „   „   „ seed 76
      „   „   „ sepals 74
      „   „   „ stamens 74
Lolium multiflorum. Italian rye-grass . . 1, 2, 9, 14, 54
  „ *perenne*. Perennial rye-grass . 9, 10, 11, 12, 56
  „ *temulentum*. Darnel rye-grass 14, 15
Lotus corniculatus. Bird's-foot trefoil 81, 86

Medicago lupulina. Trefoil 80, 88
Melica uniflora. Wood melick 14
Milium effusum. Spreading millet grass 16
Molinia caerulea. Flying bent 15, 58

Nardus stricta. Moor mat grass 12, 60

PAGE

Oats 4
Onobrychis sativa. Sainfoin 81, 94
Ornithopus perpusillus. Common bird's-foot . . . 81, 92

Palatability of grasses 10
Permanent ley 114
Persistency of grasses 9
Phleum pratense. Timothy grass . . . 2, 9, 11, 17, 62
Plant improvement 10
Poa annua. Annual meadow grass 13, 64
" *pratensis.* Smooth-stalked meadow grass . . 13, 66
" *trivialis.* Rough-stalked meadow grass . . . 13, 68
Poterium Sanguisorba. Lesser Burnet 96
Productivity of grasses 9

Rye 4

Sesleria. Blue moor grass 13
Sieglingia decumbens. Mountain heath grass . . 13, 70

Temporary ley 114
Trifolium dubium. Yellow suckling clover . . . 80, 98
" *hybridum.* Alsike clover 80, 100
" *incarnatum.* Crimson clover . . . 80, 102
" *medium.* Zigzag clover 80
" *pratense.* Wild red clover 80, 104
" *pratense.* Broad red clover 80, 106
" *pratense.* Late-flowering red clover . . 80, 106
" *repens.* Wild white clover 80, 108
" *subterraneum.* Subterranean clover . . 80, 110
Trisetum flavescens. Golden oat grass 15, 72

Vicia cracca. Tufted vetch 81
" *sativa.* Common vetch 81, 112
" *sepium.* Bush vetch 81

Wheat 2, 4
Winter greenness of grasses 10

PRINTED IN GREAT BRITAIN BY JARROLD AND SONS, LTD., NORWICH